THE BARN OWL
IN THE BRITISH ISLES

Its Past, Present and Future

by Colin R Shawyer

With all best wishes

[signature]

The Hawk Trust
London

British Library Cataloguing in Publication Data.

Shawyer, Colin R.
The barn owl in the British Isles: its past, present and future.
1. Barn owl
I. Title
598'.97   QL696.S85

ISBN 0–9503187–2–8

Text set in 9/10 Linotronic 300 Bembo, printed and bound in Great Britain at Quadrant Offset Ltd, Hertford.

The Hawk Trust wishes to acknowledge the special contribution made by the Country Landowners' Association, the Office Cleaning Services (OCS) Group and the World Wildlife Fund for the generous grants they have made towards this project.

CONTENTS

FOREWORD by Sir David Attenborough   v
AUTHOR'S PREFACE   vii
AUTHOR'S ACKNOWLEDGEMENTS   ix
INTRODUCTION by George B. Blaker   xi

PART I – THE PAST   1
  THE BARN OWL IN PRE-HISTORY   1
  HISTORICAL PERSPECTIVE   1
    The Barn Owl Between 1750 and 1800   1
    1800-1900   2
    The Period from 1900-1932   3
    The Barn Owl in England and Wales in 1932   6
    The Period After 1932   7
  SUMMARY   9

PART II – CLIMATE AND SHORT–TERM
FLUCTUATIONS IN BARN OWL NUMBERS   11
  INTRODUCTION   11
    Prolonged Snowcover   12
    Heavy and Continuous Rainfall   13
    Drought   13
  SOURCE MATERIALS AND METHODS   13
    Estimates of Annual Population Trends   13
    Climatic Research   13
  RESULTS   14
    Population Decline in Years of Climatic Extremes   14
    Mild Winters   15
  DISCUSSION   18
  SUMMARY   18

PART III – THE PRESENT   21
  THE CURRENT POPULATION LEVEL IN THE
    BRITISH ISLES   21
  HABITAT SELECTION   26
    The Influence of Altitude   26
    The Optimum Habitat Type   26
    The Supreme Importance of Grassland Edge   27
    The Size of Territories   27
    The Choice of Roosting Sites   30
  NEST SITE SELECTION   30
    Climatic Influences   30
    Imprinting on Nest Sites   37
    The Choice of Tree Species   37
    The Choice of Man-made Structures   40
    Multiple-Breeding at a Single Site   41
    Fidelity to Breeding Sites   41
  BREEDING PERFORMANCE   41
    Comparison of Productivity over the Last Fifty Years   41
    Productivity in Britain between 1982-1986   44
    Comparative Productivity in England and Wales and in Scotland   44
    Comparative Breeding Performance in Europe   44
  THE DECLINE OF THE BARN OWL OVER THE
    LAST FIFTY YEARS   47
  PRIMARY CAUSES   47
    The Effect of Climate   47
    Effects of a Reduced Food Supply   52
    The Effects of a Loss in Habitat Continuity   55

SECONDARY CAUSES   56
    Roadway Development and Urbanisation   56
    The Loss of Nest Sites and Increased Human Activity   56
    Insecticides and Rodenticides   58
    Competition with the Tawny Owl   63
MORTALITY   64
    Causes of Mortality   65
    Seasonal Mortality   70

PART IV – CONSERVATION   73
    INTRODUCTION: THE SPECIES IN LAW   73
    DETERMINING THE THREAT TO THE BARN OWL
      ON A REGIONAL BASIS   73
    CONSERVATION PLAN FOR THE BRITISH ISLES   74
    OTHER CONSERVATION ISSUES   81
    FUTURE RECOMMENDATIONS   83

APPENDIX I – World Distribution   85
APPENDIX II – Survey Methods   87
APPENDIX III – Nest Site Analysis Summary   93
APPENDIX IV – Irish Taxidermists' Records 1887–1896   97
APPENDIX V – Post-Mortem Findings   99
APPENDIX VI – Nestbox Construction and Siting   101

HISTORICAL BIBLIOGRAPHY   103
GENERAL BIBLIOGRAPHY   107

LIST OF FIGURES
  1. Barn Owl population trends 1760–1985   8
  2. Indices of population and mortality   12
  3. Climate, vole numbers and Barn Owl population levels   16
  4. Altitude of Barn Owl nest sites   26
  5. Rainfall and nest site selection   36
  6. Barn Owl hunting habitats   38
  7. Clutch size and fledging success   43
  8. Snowcover exceeding 20 days in the British Isles   50
  9. Fifteen year moving average of snowcover in the British Isles   50
10. Combine harvesters in Great Britain   53
11. Horses used for agriculture in Great Britain   54
12. Comparison of nest site selection 1932 and 1982–1985   57
13. Causes of Barn Owl mortality in England, Wales and Scotland   69
14. Causes of Barn Owl mortality in Ireland   69
15. Monthly analysis of Barn Owl mortality   71
16. Monthly analysis of female Barn Owl mortality   71
17. Monthly analysis of male Barn Owl mortality   71
18. Barn Owl deaths by drowning and road casualties   71
19. Barn Owl deaths by starvation   71

LIST OF MAPS
  1. Population density of the Barn Owl in 1900   4
  2. Barn Owl persecution in 1900   5
  3. Tawny Owl population in 1900   5
  4. Population density of the Barn Owl in 1932   22
  5. Population density of the Barn Owl 1982–1985   23
  6. Nest site selection   34
  7. Annual rainfall   35
  8. Population decline 1932–1985   48
  9. Days snowcover   49
10. January temperature   49
11. Altitude   51
12. 'Second generation' rodenticide usage   62
13. Barn Owl strongholds   75
14. Survey sample areas   88
15. Watsonian Vice-counties of Great Britain   113

LIST OF TABLES

1. Correlation of Barn Owl population minima and climate — 17
2. Vice-county population estimates — 24
3. Major types of nest site — 31
4. Type of building — 31
5. Species of tree — 32
6. Position within agricultural building — 32
7. Position within domestic building — 32
8. Average clutch size and fledging rate — 42
9. Comparison of clutch size and fledging rate — 42
10. Frequency of clutch size and fledging rate — 42
11. Percentage fledging success in Europe — 43
12. Rodenticide incidents — 67
13. Rodenticide products — 80

LIST OF COLOUR PLATES

1. A Barn Owl returns at sunset — x
2. Barn Owl at old building — 28
3. Barn Owls at tree site — 29
4. Barn Owls at cliff site — 29
5. Barn Owl emerging from old chimney — 45
6. Family of four owlets — 46
7. The signs of a well-used Barn Owl roost — 46
8. Ideal hunting habitat in traditional farmland — 78
9. Drainage ditch in Lincolnshire — 79
10. Rough grassland margin — 79
11. An old farmstead in southern England — 79
12. Computer screen showing a single record — 90
13. Computer screen showing 10-km squares — 90
14. Outline computer map of Cornwall — 90

ENGRAVING

The engraving 'Barn Owls at Home' by G.E. Lodge (1895)
is reproduced by kind permission of Major B. Booth and the Tryon Gallery — 1

FOREWORD

The Barn Owl is one of our most familiar birds, instantly recognisable by almost everyone, even by those who maintain that they have no knowledge of natural history. It is one of that small group of birds that have elected to take up residence alongside our own settlements and so has gained a particular place in our affections. For centuries, farmers have built special windows in their barns to allow the birds to enter and build their nests within, and many of us, exploring an old barn, will have had our hearts jump into our mouths when a sudden, unearthly snoring noise has come from a ledge, high in the gloom above the piles of hay, warning us not to get too near the nestlings.

How surprising and alarming it is, therefore, to discover that the Barn Owl has now become one of our rarest breeding birds. The statistics in this report make that sadly but incontrovertibly clear. Colin Shawyer and his small team have produced one of the most detailed and thorough reports ever made of any British bird. They laboured for over four years to gather over ten thousand reports. They plotted every known nest site on the National Grid to an accuracy of one square kilometre, and they gave their survey a historical dimension by re-examining and re-interpreting the statistics gathered by earlier workers. As a result, we now know that the number of Barn Owls in this country has more than halved during the last fifty years. Worse, it is still dwindling.

There was a time, not so long ago, when the British countryside was sufficiently extensive and thinly populated for no native animal or plant to need man's help to survive. Nearly all were able to do so even when man interfered with them or persecuted them. But that is no longer the case. Now the human population of these islands has grown so greatly that the demand for land – for agriculture, for houses, for motor-ways, for that most profligate and sinister category beloved by some industrialists and known as 'green-field sites' – is daily more urgent, more clamorous. The natural world can no longer rely on sufficient unwanted corners for its survival. So now we must start making choices. We must decide what it is that we want our countryside to contain and to take positive steps to make sure that it does so. Surely the Barn Owl is one of those species that we should treasure. Who can doubt that its disappearance would be a grave impoverishment of the natural scene?

The conservation of any endangered species is not likely to be successful without an intimate knowledge of its natural history. Only too often, in the past, we have not realised the full extent of our ignorance about an animal before it was urgently necessary to mount a campaign to save it, and sometimes in consequence the results have not been as effective as they should have been. That need not be the case with the Barn Owl. This meticulous and painstaking survey means that the Barn Owl, in addition to being one of our best-loved birds, is now one of our best-known. It contains all the information necessary for a plan to ensure the bird's survival. If we still want to thrill to the sight of one of them, ghostly in the evening twilight, floating along a hedgerow with slow silent wing-flaps as it hunts for its evening meal, then we have to take steps to help it.

David Attenborough

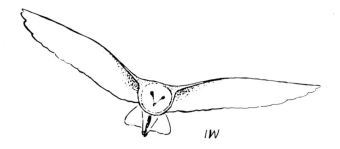

Dedicated to Emilie, Matthew and my wife Valerie without whose untiring help, encouragement and unfailing patience, this Survey could never have been accomplished.

Special Acknowledgement

I shall be forever grateful to my close friends Peter and Timothy Banks who together devoted hundreds of hours devising, refining and implementing a sophisticated computer programme which dramatically transformed this Survey and brought it out of the 'dark ages'.

It is a pleasure to add an extra thank you to Peter for sorting and analysing the many thousands of records and for reading and making invaluable comments on the manuscript. Also for our many stimulating discussions which have sown the seeds for a number of thoughts, one of which we later coined 'The Banks' Rainfall and Nest Selection Hypothesis'.

AUTHOR'S PREFACE

There is little doubt that as man places greater pressure on wild species through habitat deprivation and persecution, there comes a moral obligation to help secure the future of diminishing populations by direct human intervention.

Sometimes the methods used to try and effect change are subtle, but more often they are high-pressured and radical in an attempt to force this change. Whilst the large powerful conservation lobbies have their own important role to play, true long-lasting commitment to protection is rarely achieved through controversial legislation or bureaucracy and sometimes serves not to protect but to hasten destruction.

Farming, forestry and game-rearing are today under continual pressure from this lobby. Yet what is often forgotten is that it is the countrymen in these professions who are the major custodians of our countryside and its wildlife and as such they largely determine its future. How much better to work with them rather than against them in an attempt to secure their long-lasting commitment to the wildlife they manage, and to encourage those who remain less than sympathetic to appreciate that what they have is valuable and needs their protection.

My own policy has always been to work closely and honestly with the men of the land who overnight can influence conservation fortunes. Conservation propaganda, which sometimes seeks to exaggerate the extent or causes of a species' disappearance, whilst often reinforcing the opinions of the converted, rarely serves to encourage professional countrymen to take up the cause. It is after all they who are often more expert and better placed to judge the true situation. They are the ones upon whom we must finally rely.

The Barn Owl Survey of Britain and Ireland set out from its earliest beginnings in 1982 not simply to gather information but to carry with it a powerful educational message to encourage the active involvement of farmers, gamekeepers and all countrymen, on the basis that what is worth reporting and recording must also be worth protecting. Eleven thousand letters bear testimony to their enthusiasm, interest and genuine concern for this bird.

Just as game management, timber production and efficient farming require research to ensure greater yields, so endangered species need careful study to establish the extent of dwindling populations and the most effective ways in which they may be better helped to survive. There are of course obvious pitfalls in attempting to reduce matters of nature to a simple mathematical formula of the type which is today so often sought by governments to assess the value of a landscape or its wildlife. Whilst subjective opinion is considered of little value in science, the emotional or spiritual vision of 'old hushwing' drifting in dreamy silence over a misty Norfolk meadow is a treasure which becomes impossible to price or enumerate.

Although the survey is based upon solid and methodically researched facts, it is hoped that the many thousands who have contributed will realise that their longhand, often emotive accounts of 'their' Barn Owls were valued in many ways more highly than the cold details provided on computerised statements of fact, and that both the emotive and scientific have contributed equally to this work.

I unhesitatingly admit that the naivety with which I began this survey was rapidly transformed into a frightening realisation that a study of such magnitude and potential importance was not worth conducting if it was based on half-truths and only moderate commitment. I hope I have emerged after five years and over 6,000 hours of work with something to contribute, and that the many friends I have made will feel that their often hard-won data has served some useful purpose.

My wish is that the findings in this report can go some way to encouraging others to take up the conservation measures which can best contribute to this bird's survival in our modern world. My own desires will have been well served if our children's children are allowed the continued opportunity to seek out those quiet retreats where they can still wonder in amazement at the Barn Owl's beauty and its enchanting ways.

'A long hard climb is rewarded, I reach the top
Old gnarled rafters nearly four hundred years old.
In the corner four white balls of swansdown fluff
Eight button-black eyes gaze consciously at a large figure
Hissing aggressively as they do so.
Such young bodies with sad old faces.
No proper home, just scrapings of earth
Hundreds of pellets strewn across the floor
Parents away looking for mice and voles
I stand wondering
If owls have lived there as long as the house.'

Simon (aged 9)

AUTHOR'S ACKNOWLEDGEMENTS

My special thanks must first go to The Hawk Trust which, at its Annual General Meeting in 1982, invited me to organise its Barn Owl Survey of Britain and Ireland; subsequently for the support of all my colleagues in the Trust, not least of all Anthony Boosey and Jane Fenton who chaired the Committee throughout the course of this survey. I am also grateful to Howard Swann and Russell Coope who, having long recognised the need for such a study, instigated this enquiry; and especially to Howard who so generously provided me with unrestricted access to his vast library of often rare and valuable books.

I owe a great deal to Tony Warburton who enriched my understanding of the Barn Owl at that AGM in 1982, encouraged me to begin the survey, and has supported me ever since. Warmest thanks go to Jack Orchel who at the same event was the first to offer me his help and support and as a result of dedicated field work and conservation expertise, has throughout contributed a wealth of information, provided his photographs for this report and made valuable criticisms of the final manuscript.

Very special thanks are given to Ian Willis whose passionate interest in the Barn Owl is reflected so well in his delicately drawn illustrations; and to Colin Fairweather who not only provided data but so generously offered his superb photographs which grace these pages. Further thanks go to David Cobham whose deep affections for this owl resulted in our close association at an early stage and who has more recently provided invaluable help and advice on the publication of the report.

I would like to offer my gratitude to John Cooper who conducted The Hawk Trust's detailed pathological investigations on the many Barn Owl specimens which were submitted and for so kindly providing a summary of his findings which are included here.

I owe major thanks also to Sue Corbett who has untiringly handled the vast volume of mail over the last four years and to Amber Carroll who wrote so many articles to encourage the public's support. Also particular thanks to Peter Stewart who gave so much of his time to researching the published ringing records which form the basis of a number of observations contained within this publication.

Special thanks also to Graham Lenton whose friendship and expertise I value greatly, and Martin Holmes (Zootech Surveys) who so expertly and efficiently gathered a large volume of data from Scotland. My gratitude to Eric Hardy who provided me with invaluable information, especially relating to the Barn Owl census of 1932 with which he was involved.

Whilst it would be impossible to list all 11,000 respondents, I would nevertheless like to give individual thanks to those who (often through their county bird clubs), made enormous efforts to co-ordinate local and county surveys:

N. Atkinson, W. Barrett, I. Brice, D. Bramall, D. Brown, D. Browne, R. Bullock, P. Burman, P. Burton, A. Bury, S. Christophers, J. Clark, T. Collins, T. Copp, R. Cottis, B. Creagen, B. Curtis, P. Davies, T. Dixon, P. Dillon, A. Dobbs, M. Dorgan, R. Dunnett, Col. N. Faithful, M. Fearns, J. Franklin, H. Frost, J. Gloyn, R. Goater, W. Hampshire, A. Henderson, A. Heryet, A. Hughes, K. Hunter, J. Jackson, the late R. Jackson, J. James, S. Jeacock, P. Johnson, M. Jones, J. Kinsley, G. Kelly, R. Key, D. Leesley, D. Lewis, J. Lewis, Major N. Lewis, J. Lough, G. Madge, M. Marshall, J. Martin, John Martin, G. Mawson, J. Maxwell-Allan, W. McCulloch, G. McGeoch, D. McGrath, J. Miller, I. Morgan, D. Moss, B. Mumford, P. Newport, B. Nightingale, J. Nickson, D. Owen, I. Pennie, S. Pittam, D. Ramsden, G. Renhill, G. Rees, R. Richards, M. Ridgway, G. Ross, David Scott, Derick Scott, R. Sheppard, M. Shrubb, C. Smal, A. Smith, K. Smith, R. Smith, I. Spence, C. Sperring, P. Standley, G. Stirzaker, N. Styles, R. Turner, T. Upton, A. Village, P. Walsh, T. Weston, K. Whitehead, D. Williams and J. Williams.

I would also like to express my thanks to those who generously provided their photographs which were used so effectively to spread the conservation message and attract support for the survey at country fairs and other displays :

S.C. Brown, D. Callan, K. Carlson, S. Dalton, D. Green, J. Haywood, E. Hosking, R.T. Mills, C. Nix, W.S. Paton, A. Peach, E. Ratcliffe, D. Scott, R.T. Smith and E.K. Thompson.

I am deeply grateful to all those at the Institute of Terrestrial Ecology at Monks Wood, who have given me so much of their valuable time and allowed me to research their records. I am also indebted to the following organisations who contributed substantially to the project through the enthusiastic support of their officers, regional representatives and members:

ADAS (Farm Buildings Group), British Association for Shooting and Conservation, British Trust for Ornithology, Country Landowners' Association, Forest and Wildlife Service (IRL), Forestry Commission, Fauna and Flora Preservation Society, Farming and Wildlife Advisory Group, Game Conservancy, Hertfordshire Library Service, Irish Wildbird Conservancy, Meteorological Office, Ministry of Defence, Nature Conservancy Council, National Farmers' Union, National Trust, Royal Society for Nature Conservation (and associated County Trusts), Royal Society for the Prevention of Cruelty to Animals, Royal Society for the Protection of Birds, Scottish Wildlife Trust, Society for the Protection of Ancient Buildings, Taxidermists' Guild and the World Wildlife Fund.

My sincere thanks go to everyone who has freely provided information over the last four years, as well as those who gave publicity to the survey, for without their support there would have been nothing to report.

A very special thank you to my wife for spending many long hours typing the final manuscript from my often illegible script.

Last but not least the highlight of this four year survey was to be given the privilege of establishing a friendship with George B. Blaker CMG whose pioneering census of the Barn Owl in 1932 I had studied and admired and without which our present understanding would be seriously lacking.

1. A Barn Owl returns at sunset to feed its young in an old clock tower in Sussex.
(A. Peach)

INTRODUCTION

I am honoured indeed to have been asked to write an introduction to this impressive and immensely interesting work. It gives me joy to find that the protection of the Barn Owl from destruction as a breeding species in Britain, which seemed to me to be so much needed more than fifty years ago, has been taken up again now so competently, with renewed enthusiasm and much more knowledge and understanding than I could have brought to bear.

Colin Shawyer's careful and comprehensive survey is inspired by the same hope that I had, that effective steps could be taken to reverse the decline in the numbers of this fascinating and useful bird. His research shows, with great clarity, what needs to be done. Some of the factors involved, such as the weather, we cannot do anything about. Most of the others are due to human activity, some of it relatively new, with unpremeditated but serious effects, such as changes in agricultural practices and the huge increase in motor traffic and the building of motorways. Yet others, such as the modern trends in the development and use of rodenticides, could have been foreseen and with greater care and attention could even now to some extent be mitigated. Some losses are still due to ignorance and wilful persecution, and in this area surely there can be improvement, in accordance with the intention of the changes in the law that have been introduced in recent years.

Meanwhile the number of Barn Owls in the wild continues to dwindle, and as a nation we have a lot to do if we are to convert the potential benefits of the author's work into successful and visible results in our countryside. He makes some far-sighted suggestions as to ways in which farmers and land owners could introduce changes, as a few of them are doing, that would fundamentally improve the environment needed for the Barn Owls and in consequence also their chances of successful breeding. Have we the will to see that what can be done is adequately supported? Can we hope, in these still dark but slightly more enlightened times, when more people than ever before have begun to be aware of some of the implications of human responsibility for the state of our planet, that more people will feel able to make known their dislike of the needless slaughter, and express their pleasure and encouragement to those dwellers in the countryside who are doing what they can to see that these wonderful creatures are left unmolested in their chosen homes and are able to have the safer environment they need to live and breed in?

G. B. Blaker

xi

PART I – THE PAST

G.E. Lodge. del. et Sc.

THE BARN OWL IN PRE-HISTORY

Evidence for the presence of the Barn Owl *Tyto alba* in the British Isles in the late Devensian has been obtained from work at Cresswell Crags on the border of Derbyshire and Nottinghamshire (Jenkinson and Gilbertson 1984).

The remains of at least three individuals have been recovered from the upper levels of Pin Hole Cave in stratigraphic levels 1–4. These levels contain late upper palaeolithic artefacts which have been dated to a period about 10,000 years ago.

A rich variety of suitable prey species are associated with the Barn Owls, including four species of microtines (Common Vole *Microtus arvalis*, Short-tailed Vole *M. agrestis*, Root Vole *M. oeconomus*, and Gregarious Vole *M. gregalis*), together with considerable numbers of the Arctic Lemming *Dicrostonyx torquatus*.

A particular feature of these stratigraphic levels is the substantial evidence of the presence of frogs/toads *Rana/Bufo* spp., amounting to over three hundred individuals. Of particular interest therefore are a number of owl pellets consisting entirely of amphibian remains (Jenkinson pers.comm.). Whilst at the present time Barn Owls are known on occasion to take frogs, it is less usual for these to be the only item of diet. However, fresh pellets consisting entirely of frog remains were found at a number of separate nest sites in south-west Scotland in April 1986 during a year in which frog numbers appeared particularly high.

It was of course about 10,000 years ago, with the onset of the Pre-Boreal climatic period, that temperatures began to rise and flora and fauna began to spread north with the climatic amelioration. Recent work suggests that temperatures were in fact already higher at this time

than was originally thought. Average July temperatures may well have been approaching 16°C at Cresswell, whilst average December/January temperatures were probably not much lower than 0°C. In any case the more mobile species such as birds and insects were able to take advantage of the spread of the warmer climate more rapidly than the flora.

The Barn Owl nests today in the rock fissures at Cresswell, and it is a fascinating thought that it may have been doing so for the last 10,000 years.

HISTORICAL PERSPECTIVE

Examination of the historical records was initially required in order to put the Barn Owl's current status into perspective and to identify more fully the factors which were likely to be governing long-term population trends. Status reports from 1750 onwards are now reviewed in the context of current knowledge, and references will be found in the Historical Bibliography.

The Barn Owl between 1750 and 1800 – A period of stability and increase

Documented information prior to 1750 is generally insufficient to enable any precise conclusions to be drawn about the Barn Owl's status in the British Isles. There are however, sufficient references to indicate that it was a familiar bird during this period. Between 1750 and 1800, some of the most celebrated naturalists of the time were unanimously confirming that this owl was both widely distributed and numerous. It was for example described as 'very common in every part of Europe' (De Buffon 1770); 'very common in most of the European countries and none we believe more so than in this Kingdom' (Latham 1781); and 'It need scarcely be said that the white

1

owl is common in every part of England.....' (Donovan 1794-1819).

During the earlier part of this period open field agriculture still predominated over large regions of Britain. Because grazed livestock were prevented from straying into cornfields by tethering or herding, there was little need for the division of fields by hedgerows, although the boom in wool production had already encouraged this practice in some areas.

The drainage and enclosure of land which had previously been confined mainly to regions within East Anglia, south-west England and Wales, increased throughout Britain from 1760 as a partial consequence of the Enclosure Acts. Open fields of intermixed strips were thus rearranged and sub-divided. Between 1720 and 1845 over six million acres had been dealt with in this way (Fussell 1966). Here field sizes decreased from an average of about 32 ha in 1680 to just 6.5 ha by 1839, an area which was considered suitable for arable cultivation by horses. About 6.9 ha of the original open field was now in fact consumed by the newly created hedgerows themselves (Pollard *et al* 1974).

The subsequent emergence of boundary hedgerows and ditches, together with the opening up of woodlands and the creation of water meadows, would have greatly expanded the 'grassland edge' hunting habitat which we now know to be so important for the Barn Owl. Indeed many of the small cornfields possessed a ten foot grass walkway around their hedge-fringed edges. The expansion of corn production, for increasing human and livestock consumption, resulted in corn-ricks and straw-bedded cattle yards becoming more commonplace as part of the newly created farmsteads. This new micro-habitat provided additional shelter for an abundance of prey, thereby increasing the breeding potential and reducing the over-wintering mortality of this otherwise susceptible species.

It was most probable therefore that not only was the Barn Owl common in the latter half of the eighteenth century but increased its numbers quite rapidly during this period through to the early 1800s as additional man-made habitat emerged and changing farm methods, of a type favourable to this species, developed during the beginnings of this agricultural revolution.

1800 to 1900 – A period of high population followed by a dramatic decline

Over the earlier part of the 1800s the Barn Owl was considered to be as common, if not more common, than in the previous fifty years. Jardine (1838) described it as 'by far the most common and equally distributed species over the British Islands, very common in England and abounding in Scotland, and extending to the North, whilst it is apparently equally common in Ireland'. Further reports at this time describe the Barn Owl as 'more extensively distributed and more numerous, in Britain than any other species.... In most parts of England it is not very uncommon and the same may be said of the southern and middle divisions of Scotland' (MacGillivray 1840). In Ireland too, it was emphatically considered 'the most common species' (Thompson 1849).

During the entire period from 1750-1850, the Tawny Owl *Strix aluco* had been described as fairly common but always less so than the Barn Owl. Throughout Scotland, however, the Tawny was believed to be much less numerous. In the North it was considered rare, although some population expansion was beginning to be reported. The Long-eared Owl *Asio otus* took over as the second most common species in Scotland, as was indeed the case in Ireland where the Tawny Owl remains, to this day, a non-breeding bird.

It has now been established from a careful study of the county avifaunas which began to appear in the early part of the nineteenth century, that a noticeable decline in Barn Owl numbers had already begun throughout most of Britain around 1825 shortly after the beginnings of the pheasant-rearing era. By 1850, game-rearing had become so popular and well established in most regions, that the increasing use of the pole trap and the invention of the breech-loading gun in 1853 had had a devastating effect on the Barn Owl population. Even as early as 1839 we find the author of The Maidstone Topography – 'deploring this senseless slaughter' (Ticehurst 1909). Taxidermy and egg collecting flourished as the Victorian era progressed. Barn Owls were prized for private collections and tradesmen were quick to exploit a source of wings for the manufacture of firescreens, and feathers for the millinery trade. So severe were the effects of persecution in some regions, that counties as far apart as Cornwall and Dumfries-shire were reporting that the Barn Owl was close to extinction by the beginning of the twentieth century.

A selection of quotations from books which were published in the second half of the nineteenth century gives some indication of the extent of this problem:

'There has been no discrimination used in the slaughter of so-called 'vermin' – Owls too the police of the stackgarth are sacrificed with equal disregard. This collection was made up of Hawks, Owls, Daws, Buzzards and such like vermin. It is now quite impossible in the north of England for a gamekeeper to form such another museum to bear testimony to his zeal and ignorance as the so-called vermin no longer exist.'

(John Handcock 1874)

'but now the useful Barn Owls are shot and trapped by short-sighted, ignorant men, and the mice multiply in consequence.'

'Thus the ignorance of man has from time immemorial attributed evil to the owls, and caused them to be regarded with suspicion and superstitious horror, and consequently to be persecuted in every way . . .;'

(The Rev Charles Smith 1887)

'a great many are nevertheless annually destroyed, being often captured in the daytime in barns and other places which they are known to frequent; I have seen as many as fifteen in a bird-stuffer's shop in May, all of which had been recently received.'

(Oliver V Aplin 1889)

'In every little bird-stuffer's shop the Barn-Owl

may be numbered by the half-dozen distorted and caricatured, his face and wings, perhaps, converted into fire screens; too often we find him rotting with crows and weasels in a keeper's larder, having been murdered by the cruel pole-trap to which, having caught his mouse, he has unsuspiciously betaken himself to devour it at leisure; while the guns of these who, if they knew their own interests, 'sua si bona norint' would best strive to protect him, are too often pointed at him.'

(William S M D'Urban and The Rev Murray A Mathew 1895)

In the wake of this persecution pressure came a succession of fifteen hard winters between 1860-1900, the severity of which had not been known in the previous fifty years and which have never again occurred. These would have been devastating for a species whose numbers were already under threat.

The pattern of farming too was once again becoming less favourable to the Barn Owl as the agricultural revolution progressed during a period of enormous prosperity. As the factory production of farm implements increased, underground drainage was invented, and the practical application of steam power for threshing and ploughing began, field sizes once again became enlarged. Ditches, together with the hedges and hedgerow timber which had so recently been developed, were now being removed. Both of these factors would have undoubtedly offset any improvement which might have been anticipated from the gradual relaxation of persecution as this century drew to its close.

The first evidence of any improvement in human attitudes towards this bird appeared in a few county reports around 1880, at a time which heralded the first stirrings of a greater awareness and understanding of birds of prey generally and the Barn Owl in particular. A number of statements appeared in the literature re-emphasising the economic importance of the species for controlling farm rodent pests. These, coupled with the introduction of the bird protection laws (which began in Northumberland in 1869 and 1872 and which led to the Wild Birds Protection Act in 1880), together with legislation outlawing the pole trap in 1904, were collectively responsible for increasing public awareness and for reducing the number of Barn Owls killed.

The earliest opportunity of providing any meaningful baseline of Barn Owl abundance in Britain came towards the end of the nineteenth century, by which time the majority of counties in England and a number in Wales had published their own avifaunas. Whilst the authors of these historic works were unable to present any numerical indication of the Barn Owl's status, most provided a descriptive assessment of the bird's standing in their respective counties by the late 1800s.

Using these references it is possible to estimate the status of the Barn Owl (and Tawny Owl) in most counties of Britain with some degree of confidence. Four categories of abundance have been assigned ranging from common to scarce. The relative abundance of the Barn Owl (and Tawny Owl) for each county has been derived mainly from the entries for the species in these publications, together with any other relevant details contained within the introductions or appendices. In the few counties where there was any substantial doubt or insufficient information about these species' status then this has been estimated using data from adjoining counties. Maps 1, 2 and 3 summarise the findings of a detailed literature search of county avifaunas and local reports published in England, Wales and Ireland during the period 1880-1919 and in Scotland between 1871-1929.

It immediately becomes apparent that although the majority of counties had reported a decline in Barn Owl numbers, a marked regional difference in the species' relative abundance had emerged by about 1900. In the counties of the South-west and in parts of East Anglia, the Barn Owl was now considered scarce or uncommon. It is significant that in about 80% of the counties within these regions, persecution in the name of game preservation was being cited by the authors of these books as the sole cause of the Barn Owl's accelerating decline. In the South-east, however, this owl was remarkably common. Here its population had also experienced much less decline, and in contrast to the regions elsewhere, there was rarely any mention that persecution had been implicated.

It can clearly be seen that the regions of high Barn Owl abundance closely mirror those where persecution was least severe (Map 2). Unlike the situation with other birds of prey, many of which were even more intensively persecuted, the Barn Owl's regional fortunes were very much dictated by the contradictory nature of local superstition, legend and the extent of general awareness about the usefulness of the bird. These beliefs either served to reinforce its destruction, or in other regions encouraged some degree of protection.

Maps 1 and 3 also indicate that although the Barn Owl was still considered to be the more common species throughout south-east Britain in the late 1800s, the Tawny Owl had by now taken over as the more numerous species in the South-west and in the North. This was undoubtedly due to the comparative ease with which the Barn Owl could be found and persecuted at its daytime roost. The Tawny Owl on the other hand survived better in these high risk areas because of its more secretive and nocturnal nature. The comparative stability of the Barn Owl population in the South-east was probably also the result of the abundance of corn-ricks on farmland in these corn-producing counties. These ricks would have provided the additional shelter and surpluses of prey necessary for survival during the winters of 1860-1900, which were noted for their countrywide severity.

The Period from 1900 to 1932

By the beginning of the twentieth century, some recovery in numbers was being reported, albeit only in the more northern regions of England in Northumberland and Durham, together with the counties of southern Scotland: Berwickshire, the Lothians and Fife and a little later Dumfries-shire. Numbers throughout the rest of Britain however, were showing no noticeable improvement.

In complete contrast to the extreme severity of the winters between 1860-1900, the new century began with a succession of remarkably mild winters which were to continue for almost forty years. It was these relatively

3

Map 1 *The population status of the Barn Owl in 1900.*

This summary was compiled from the information contained in county avifaunas and local reports published in England, Wales and Ireland between 1880–1919, and in Scotland from 1871–1929. For the references used in the construction of this map see Historical Bibliography and Appendix IV.

Common
Fairly Common
Uncommon
Scarce

4

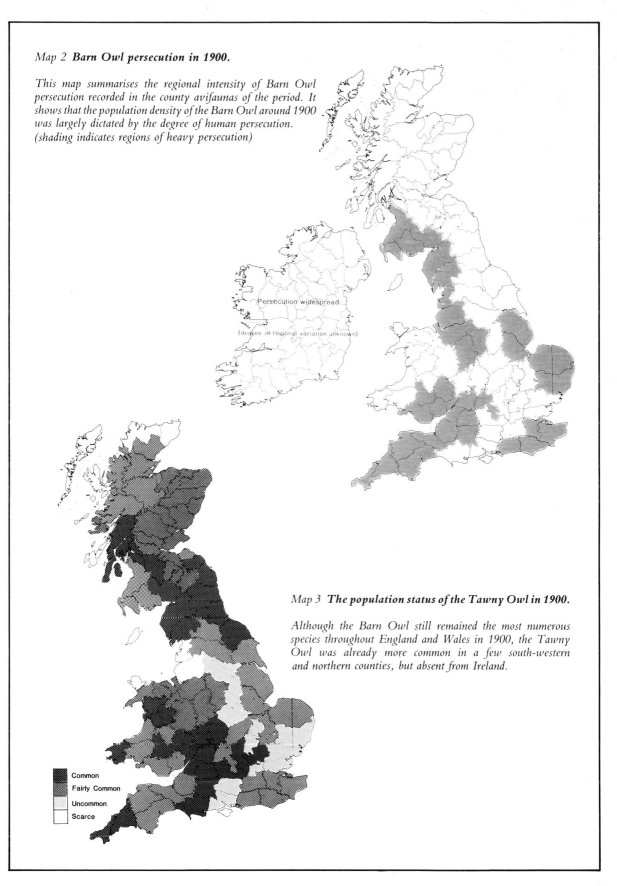

Map 2 **Barn Owl persecution in 1900.**

This map summarises the regional intensity of Barn Owl persecution recorded in the county avifaunas of the period. It shows that the population density of the Barn Owl around 1900 was largely dictated by the degree of human persecution. *(shading indicates regions of heavy persecution)*

Persecution widespread

(degree of regional variation unknown)

Map 3 **The population status of the Tawny Owl in 1900.**

Although the Barn Owl still remained the most numerous species throughout England and Wales in 1900, the Tawny Owl was already more common in a few south-western and northern counties, but absent from Ireland.

Common
Fairly Common
Uncommon
Scarce

5

snow-free years which were undoubtedly the major factor responsible for the recovery in the Barn Owl population in north-east Britain, for it would have been here, close to the northern limit of the species' world range, that the marked amelioration in the winter climate would have been most felt.

Some evidence for what was to prove a short-lived recovery in Britain came during the 1914-1918 war, when naturalists were writing about the general increase in raptors brought about by the reduction in keepering. The techniques and recording of bird ringing were not yet, however, sufficiently well-developed to allow any empirical interpretations to be made about the increase in Barn Owl numbers during this period.

As soon as the war was over, and many keepers re-employed, the Barn Owl population once again appeared to fall into some decline in spite of less intensive land use and the favourably mild winters

The Barn Owl in England and Wales in 1932 – The First Nationwide Census

In 1932 George B. Blaker made the first serious attempt to census the Barn Owl in England and Wales. This year also saw the beginnings of a national ringing and recording scheme which differentiated for the first time between the numbers of adults and nestlings ringed and thereafter provided a more meaningful interpretation of annual fluctuations in Barn Owl numbers.

George Blaker first appeared in the ornithological literature in 1932 when, as a student at Eton, he was awarded the RSPB Silver Medal in the Public School Essay Competition for an essay entitled 'The Barn Owl and the Buzzard' (Blaker 1932). It was however at Trinity College, Cambridge that his pioneering census of the Barn Owl in England and Wales was conducted on behalf of the Royal Society for the Protection of Birds, for which he was later awarded the Gold Medal in 1934 (Blaker 1933, 1934).

This census was undertaken at a time when the network of ornithologists and media publicity was clearly much less developed than it is today. It involved a species which remains one of the three most difficult birds to census . Nevertheless the qualities of enthusiasm and attention to detail were to make this the most detailed national bird census of its time, providing to this day the only baseline with which the population trends of this species can be compared. Blaker's enquiry had been prompted by naturalists' suspicions that for several years prior to 1932, the Barn Owl was beginning to show a noticeable decline in numbers.

The study, which began in May 1932 and ended in December of that year, enlisted the help of societies, clubs, individual naturalists and the general public with the aid of publicity both local and national, using a well-worded questionnaire, accompanying map and bird identification guide. It sought detailed nest site data from those ornithologists willing to undertake local field surveys, together with more generalised information, mainly in letter form from the public.

Each field worker was allotted an observer number and each region an area code. The questionnaire was designed for the field specialist and requested the following information: nest site description, date of first visit, clutch size, brood size, fledging success, frequency of adults carrying food to the nest site, together with the locations and dates of any other Barn Owls seen in the allotted areas. It also sought data relating to the availability of potential nesting places, the extent of recruitment of Barn Owls within, and dispersal out of the area, and where numbers were considered to have decreased, an opinion as to the cause. (Shawyer 1985. Census Form A. Barn Owl Census 1932 – Archive data.)

As a result of these enquiries, 915 detailed nest site descriptions were received from between fifty and one hundred field workers (Hardy pers.comm.). From these, 214 records of breeding success were obtained. These data were supplemented by generalised information of a more subjective nature, from approximately 4,000 further observers. An excess of 5,000 breeding records eventually provided the basis for estimating the species' abundance in England and Wales (Blaker pers. comm.). This information was originally illustrated as a map of England and Wales sub-divided into Vice-counties. The Barn Owl's abundance was shown for each 10-mile square. For the purposes of comparison with the present *Survey* in Part III of this report, this map has been redrawn on the basis of 10-km squares (Map 4). Blaker drew attention to the possible limitations of his survey when he stated that 'most of the conclusions arrived at are based on collective opinion … whilst we have no doubts as to the substantial correctness of the views here expressed, we claim no infallibility'.

Whatever the limitations (and the immensity of the task was bound to introduce some), his census has provided the only sound baseline in history. Some of these limitations of coverage were imposed by the times but many remain with us today, being dictated by the Barn Owl's widespread distribution and its elusive nature. It is perhaps because of these difficulties that it has taken a further fifty years before the necessary enthusiasm was regenerated and the methodology devised, to census a bird which was placed on the First Schedule of the Protection of Birds Act over twenty years ago.

The present *Survey* has now demonstrated that the Barn Owl population in the British Isles is subject to continual 3-4 year cyclical change and that these periodic fluctuations, which relate to abundance of small mammal prey, are in fact influenced by climatic extremes such as prolonged duration of winter snowcover, excessive spring rainfall and summer drought.

Blaker, not having the advantage of the data on which these conclusions are now based, would have been unaware that the Barn Owl population in the UK was subject to these regular and sometimes dramatic changes (although he had already identified the importance of the food supply in regulating Barn Owl numbers). Any population estimate, or indeed comparison with past population levels, is therefore subject to potential misinterpretation without some knowledge of the particular phase in which the cycle is operating. The implications of these temporary short-term fluctuations in Barn Owl abundance are now discussed in relation to the conclusions of the 1932 census.

Although the Barn Owl ringing data prior to 1932 was limited, because the number of birds ringed annually was small, the data were nevertheless sufficiently well documented to indicate that the population was at a low ebb between 1927 and 1929. This is likely to have been influenced firstly in 1927 by the wettest spring/summer this century and subsequently by the severe winters of both 1928 and 1929. In the absence of further climatic events, a peak of temporary Barn Owl abundance was reached in 1930, only to drop back in 1931 after another very wet spring/summer (the sixth wettest this century), finally peaking again in 1933. It would seem probable therefore, that Blaker's census in 1932 was conducted during a period when the population was on the recovery phase just prior to an all time high in 1933.

The census reported a population of 25,000 birds (12,000 pairs + 1,000 non-breeding birds) in England and Wales which, because the cycle was in a phase of recovery, would have probably represented a population figure somewhat lower than the maximum attainable during the 1930s.

The species' decline was reported by Blaker to have been gradual since 1900, becoming most noticeable in the regions of central and southern England during 1922 and 1928. From these observations, Blaker concluded that the Barn Owl population in England and Wales may have declined by as much as 33% (from 18,000 pairs) since 1922. Analysis of the meteorological data for that period indicates however, that two of the most severe climatic events this century occurred in 1921 and 1927, the years which actually preceded the two noticeable population declines. In 1921 Britain suffered the worst June/July drought since 1868 and, as previously discussed, 1927 registered the wettest summer since 1879. Indeed it remains the wettest to this day. As if this were not enough, the severe winters of 1928 and 1929 followed.

The onset of these significant declines in population which were observed in 1922 and 1928 were undoubtedly the result of the low breeding success which would have taken place during 1921 and 1927. Whilst there was unquestionably a continuation of some decline in the Barn Owl population during the period leading up to the census, the acceleration to which Blaker had alluded was probably more indicative of the type of temporary crashes with which we are now familiar and from which the population invariably shows a natural recovery.

Blaker's report emphasised that the overall decline observed in southern and central England was not being reflected in the North. Indeed, the counties of Northumberland, Cumberland and Westmorland were showing a noticeable increase. This observation was consistent with earlier reports contained in the avifaunas of these counties as well as from publications concerning the southern counties of Scotland, most of which had cited an increase in Barn Owl numbers soon after 1910. The continued improvement in the North at this time was certainly the result of a marked reduction of the winter snowfall throughout the British Isles from 1900, which would have been most significant in these colder northern districts more susceptible to snow. In addition, the recently established Forestry Commission began planting extensive areas of young forest in 1919, which led to the creation of wide expanses of rough grassland habitat in these regions. By 1920 the Barn Owl had already been observed utilising these new habitats (Paton and Pike 1929).

Summarising the factors responsible for the Barn Owl's decline in 1932, Blaker considered interference by man prominent; this in spite of the changing attitudes of an increasingly enlightened public and his own observation that 'There is a healthy tendency growing among gamekeepers to regard the Barn Owl as a valuble check on the smaller and more elusive types of vermin'. Although as we now know superstition and persecution had begun to recede in the early 1900s, reports of a sudden and major increase in the numbers of raptors during the First and Second World Wars continued to demonstrate how dependent this group of birds was on man's activities. Blaker found that there was still a market for egg and skin collecting although he drew particular attention to the fact that farmers themselves jealously guarded their Barn Owls against gamekeepers, and in some cases against the census field workers themselves.

Blaker further believed that the Barn Owl's diminishing numbers and increased diurnal activity were the result of a declining rodent population around the farmyard as a result of more efficient threshing techniques, less wasteful feeding of animals and the use of rodenticides. However, he made no claims that the loss of grassland foraging areas outside of the farmyard was to blame. Indeed it would appear that the extent of permanent grassland in Britain had substantially expanded from 11,149,000 acres in 1866 to a peak of 17,453,000 acres in 1933, an increase of 36%. (After this period of farming recession it fell back to 15,896,000 acres by 1940. Today it amounts to approximately 12,500,000 acres, close to its level a century ago)(HMSO 1968, 1986).

The loss of nesting sites was a further reason given for the birds' decline caused by the destruction of old barns and trees together with the wiring off of church towers against Jackdaws *Corvus monedula*. Weatherproof nestboxes and barrels were advocated, indeed these already featured in the list of breeding sites used in 1932.

Competition with the Tawny Owl for food and nest sites was also considered an additional cause of the species' decline. Blaker drew attention to the fact that the Tawny Owl was now more common everywhere and that the increase in the numbers of this species since 1900 appeared to have mirrored the Barn Owl's decline.

The Period After 1932

Fifty years have elapsed since the Census in 1932. During this period no serious attempts have been made to repeat this study. However in 1963 a joint BTO/NCC enquiry was organised of 'some smaller birds of prey' among which the Barn Owl was included (Prestt 1965). This work was prompted by concerns about the apparent demise of raptors in general and the recent introduction of chlorinated hydrocarbon pesticides in agriculture. The results of this enquiry confirmed the Barn Owl's moderate decrease in Lancashire and throughout eastern England (with the possible exception of Norfolk) from Yorkshire to Kent. These results have been reviewed more thoroughly in the light of present knowledge in Part III of this report.

A year later an attempt was made to assess the breeding status of the Kestrel *Falco tinnunculus*, Tawny Owl and Barn Owl in greater depth (Prestt and Bell 1966). As has been stated by Bunn *et al* (1982) 'this was something of a failure and perhaps for the first time the difficulties in locating the species began to be appreciated'.

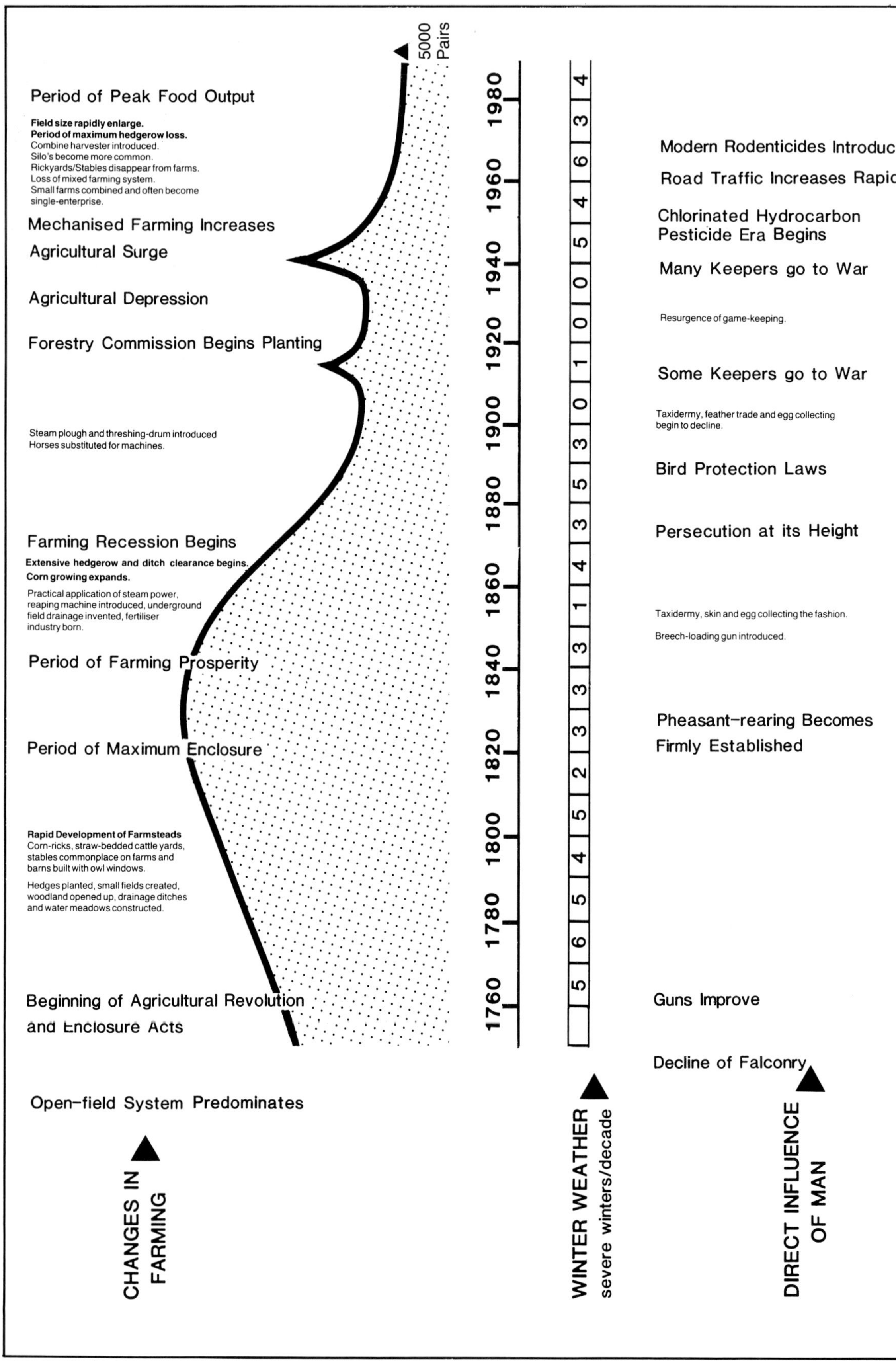

5000 Pairs

1980

1960

1940

1920

1900

1880

1860

1840

1820

1800

1780

1760

Changes in Farming column:

Period of Peak Food Output

Field size rapidly enlarge.
Period of maximum hedgerow loss.
Combine harvester introduced.
Silo's become more common.
Rickyards/Stables disappear from farms.
Loss of mixed farming system.
Small farms combined and often become
single-enterprise.

Mechanised Farming Increases

Agricultural Surge

Agricultural Depression

Forestry Commission Begins Planting

Steam plough and threshing-drum introduced
Horses substituted for machines.

Farming Recession Begins

Extensive hedgerow and ditch clearance begins.
Corn growing expands.
Practical application of steam power,
reaping machine introduced, underground
field drainage invented, fertiliser
industry born.

Period of Farming Prosperity

Period of Maximum Enclosure

Rapid Development of Farmsteads
Corn-ricks, straw-bedded cattle yards,
stables commonplace on farms and
barns built with owl windows.

Hedges planted, small fields created,
woodland opened up, drainage ditches
and water meadows constructed.

Beginning of Agricultural Revolution
and Enclosure Acts

Open-field System Predominates

CHANGES IN FARMING

Winter Weather column (severe winters/decade):

4

3

6

4

5

0

0

0

1

0

3

5

3

4

1

3

3

3

2

5

4

5

6

5

WINTER WEATHER
severe winters/decade

Direct Influence of Man column:

Modern Rodenticides Introduced

Road Traffic Increases Rapidly

Chlorinated Hydrocarbon
Pesticide Era Begins

Many Keepers go to War

Resurgence of game-keeping.

Some Keepers go to War

Taxidermy, feather trade and egg collecting
begin to decline.

Bird Protection Laws

Persecution at its Height

Taxidermy, skin and egg collecting the fashion.

Breech-loading gun introduced.

Pheasant-rearing Becomes
Firmly Established

Guns Improve

Decline of Falconry

DIRECT INFLUENCE OF MAN

Fig. 1 Barn Owl population trends 1760–1985

8

An extensive historical review of the breeding birds of Britain and Ireland by Parslow (1973) suggested that the Barn Owl population was probably within the range 1,001–10,000 pairs.

Between 1968–1972, the field work was conducted for The Atlas of Breeding Birds in Britain and Ireland (Sharrock 1976). This involved an estimated 10,000–15,000 observers. The intention was to map by 10-kilometre squares the distribution of all species breeding in the British Isles. As far as the Barn Owl was concerned, the records from England and Wales were augmented by reports received as a result of appeals on radio and in various farming and county journals. The *Atlas* showed the Barn Owl to be widely distributed except on the Pennines, the Welsh mountains and the Scottish Highlands. This monumental work was not intended to provide any detailed information about population levels. For example, once a Barn Owl pair had been confirmed nesting in a particular square no further proof was required for that square. Additional pairs which were present thus went unrecorded. A statement was nevertheless made about the overall population figure based on an estimate of 2–4 pairs for each of the 2,279 10-km squares found to be occupied. This was finally reported as 4,500–9,000 pairs in Britain and Ireland for the period 1968–1972. Whilst this could not be entirely supported by the limited data on population density, it was nevertheless likely to have been a fairly reliable assessment.

In 1969 D. Scott began an enquiry into the population density and recent changes in the Barn Owl's status in Britain. The information was subsequently passed on to Bunn, Warburton and Wilson. The enquiry was then expanded by these authors and requests for generalised information about population changes within counties were made to Regional Representatives of the BTO in 1972/73 and later in 1978/79. Whilst the authors stated that the information was extremely variable and frequently rather vague, they nevertheless presented summaries of their findings on a county basis concluding that Barn Owl numbers had declined since the period of the Atlas (Bunn *et al* 1982). The raw data from this enquiry were kindly passed on to the present author in 1982 (Shawyer 1982, Barn Owl Enquiry 1972/79 – Archive Data).

SUMMARY

Throughout the last 200 years, the Barn Owl population has been in a state of constant and often dramatic change.

We can only speculate about the actual numbers of Barn Owls present in the early days of this period, since statistical data were not recorded. Published materials however reinforce the view that the species was infinitely more common throughout the British Isles at the turn of the eighteenth century than it has been at any time since. Indeed, it is probable that numbers increased during the late 1700s as the enclosure of land advanced and farmsteads sprang up.

After about 1820, a progressive decline in the Barn Owl population began, which accelerated rapidly as game-rearing became a major part of country life. This led to the employment of gamekeepers, and together with the introduction of the breech-loading gun resulted in more efficient methods of predator control. By the 1870s, the disappearance of many birds of prey stimulated a more enlightened public attitude towards the Barn Owl, although the Victorian age of specimen collecting was far from over. Recovery was therefore slow in the latter years of the nineteenth century, probably compounded by the serious deterioration in the winter weather which began in the 1860s and lasted until the end of the century.

A temporary overall increase in numbers was recorded during the First World War. Later on, whilst some regions of Britain were showing a distinct recovery at the time of the first population census in 1932, elsewhere there was little indication of any improvement. This was in spite of a substantial expansion in the total area of permanent grassland (as a consquence of farming recession), and over thirty years of mild winters. The population in 1932 was thus reported at 12,000 pairs. The population trends from the late 1700s are summarised in Figure 1.

Until the present *Survey*, no attempt had been made to repeat a population census. The few enquiries which did include this species suggested a rapidly declining, but nevertheless fluctuating downward trend. This began in the early 1940s, declined sharply until the mid 1950s and continued, albeit at a lower rate, into the 1980s (Figure 3).

This summary concludes the findings of this historical research and brings us to the present day. However, before discussing the results of the 1982–1985 Barn Owl Survey of Britain and Ireland, Part II of this report investigates the causes of the temporary fluctuations in numbers which, as we are now aware, are a notable feature of the breeding biology of the Barn Owl in the British Isles.

PART II – CLIMATE AND SHORT-TERM FLUCTUATIONS IN BARN OWL NUMBERS

INTRODUCTION

This part of the report aims to explain more fully the causes of the short-term fluctuations in Barn Owl numbers and provides a basis for differentiating between these temporary changes and the factors which have been governing the species' long-term decline.

The Barn Owl population in the British Isles has been experiencing a sustained decline since the mid-1800s. Superimposed on this long-term decrease are annual fluctuations in abundance which, although often dramatic in effect, are rapidly self-correcting and of a temporary nature. A failure to understand the factors governing these short-term fluctuations has previously given rise to misconceptions about the origins and intensity of the Barn Owl's long-term decline this century.

Climate is the fundamental natural influence governing a species' population by regulating the availability of food and shelter. The climate of the British Isles is noted for its short-term variability. Sustained sequences of severe types of weather are rare. Animal communities tend therefore to adjust to the capricious nature of our climate. Nevertheless for the Barn Owl, which in the British Isles is at the northern limit of its world range, even small changes in climate could be expected to play a major role in regulating population levels. The most important consequences of climatic extremes are those which influence the availability of food; either by reducing small mammal populations directly or by decreasing the bird's efficiency in capturing prey. The latter commonly arises when small mammals become inaccessible under a blanket of snow or when hunting is inhibited by prolonged periods of rain.

The Barn Owl, unlike the other species of European owl, is particularly vulnerable to a reduced food supply and is capable of exhausting accumulated fat reserves within as little as eight days. In healthy specimens these fat reserves are as low as 5.4-5.6% of total body weight (Piechocki 1960). This low safety margin precludes long survival under unfavourable conditions of the type experienced in the more severe winter regimes of central and northern Europe, where the mean January isotherm is below that in Britain and snowcover is more prolonged. The population dynamics of the less sedentary eastern European sub-species, *T. a. guttata,* have been extensively studied in terms of the incidents of mass winter mortality which have been recorded regularly since 1921. Most specimens examined at the time of these winter incidents were severely emaciated, a condition which has been linked to the status of the vole cycle (Honer 1963).

In the British Isles there is no statistical evidence from the numbers of specimens received by the British Trust for Ornithology (BTO) Ringing Scheme for any increase in annual mortality even during the most severe winters of 1939/40, 1946/47, 1962/63 and 1978/79. A detailed analysis of the records of 200 taxidermists which provide substantially more annual mortality data than that of the BTO's scheme, likewise confirms this view. (However, Ticehurst (1948) and Dobinson (1964) found some indication of increased mortality during the two exceptionally harsh winters of 1946/47 and 1962/63.)

Yet a further indication that winter severity appears to

play little part in substantially increasing direct mortality emerges from an analysis of the numbers of Barn Owl specimens received by the Institute of Terrestrial Ecology, Monks Wood, Cambs., in response to their pesticide monitoring study between 1963 and 1977. In Figure 2, July-June mortality totals are plotted alongside an index of annual Barn Owl population levels derived from the ringing totals compiled by the BTO. Here it can be seen that the years of peak mortality simply reflect those years when high breeding productivity occurred. Conversely, in the very severe winters of 1963, 1966, 1969, 1970 and the extreme drought year of 1976, mortality far from showing any increase was in fact at its lowest level in each of these five years.

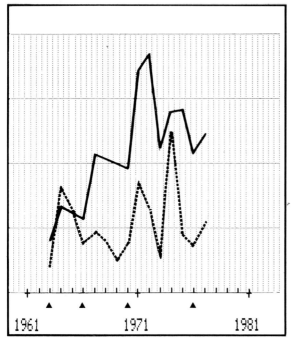

Fig. 2 *Number of carcases received at Monks Wood Experimental Station, Cambridgeshire, each year (broken line), alongside the annual population index derived from ringing records of the British Trust for Ornithology (solid line). Arrows indicate years of climatic extremes.*

A more significant level of mortality must nevertheless arise with those birds occupying marginal upland habitats where snowcover becomes more prolonged with increasing altitude.

Throughout the British Isles in general, however, and especially in the southern and western regions where the winter climate is somewhat milder than that experienced in much of central Europe, the Barn Owl is less susceptible to winter starvation . This is undoubtedly explained by the fact that over 80% of the breeding population currently breed below 125 m in the warmer, more sheltered lowland valleys where they are cushioned from the effects of all but the hardest of winters. However, less typical avian and invertebrate prey species are more commonly taken as food at these times.

Pellet samples analysed from a number of regions throughout the British Isles during a period when snow

had lain continuously for 15 – 20 days in 1982/83 and 1985/86, indicated that survival could be maintained on as little as 17.5 g per 12 hours. (Sparrows, Starlings *Sturnus vulgaris* and House Mice *Mus musculus* were the most common verterbate prey items, although at some locations beetles comprised the major proportion of the diet). Pellet samples collected at other times during the year from 52 widely scattered localities between 1982 and 1985 indicated that the average prey content per pellet was 66.4 g or 3.4 prey items. (Maximum 140 g, 14 prey items; minimum 26.1 g, less than one prey item). Comparison of these two sets of figures suggests that Barn Owls may be capable of surviving on less than one third of their normal daily requirements for up to 20 days during times of prolonged food shortage.

In the British Isles, increased mortality appears to be a less significant consequence of extreme climatic conditions. The influence of weather on the Barn Owl's breeding potential is now considered in terms of the temporary but often dramatic population fluctuations which commonly occur with this species.

Prolonged Snowcover

Winter snowfall is normally heaviest and most prolonged during the months of January, February and March, and it is during early March that the female becomes sexually active and courtship commences. In order for this to be successful, the female must receive a surfeit of food from the male. The presentation of food is almost always the trigger for copulation which occurs repeatedly throughout the evenings from March to May. It would seem likely therefore, that if food is in short supply, as a consequence of prolonged winter snow (or sustained rainfall), then the opportunity for successful fertilisation becomes much reduced. Not only this, but a depleted food supply caused by the earlier occurrence of heavy snows in January and February can prevent the birds from accumulating the necessary reserves to attain peak breeding condition in time for egg-laying during late April or early May.

In the Tawny Owl, it is already known that egg-laying needs to be preceded as early as December by an accumulation of fat reserves, the level of which may be critical in determining whether or not breeding eventually takes place. Weight in this species is therefore not only a positive indicator of ovarian development but should these levels of fat be insufficient in March, then final ovulation does not appear to proceed. An increase in male testes size can also be related to body condition in terms of protein levels, and this too is dependent on an optimal food supply in the winter months prior to breeding (Hirons 1985; Hirons *et al* 1984). In Barn Owls too, there is also evidence for a higher weight requirement during the months from December to March (Hardy, *et al* 1981).

The Barn Owl with its especially frail fat reserves is therefore likely to be particularly vulnerable during the most severe of winter months between January and March. This is a time when the birds are attempting to reach prime condition in preparation for courtship and fertilisation, thence in April and May to egg-laying, incubation and early brooding, over which period the female is entirely dependent on the male for food.

Heavy and Continuous Rainfall

The effects of heavy and continuous rainfall especially in spring can substantially reduce the hunting ability of the Barn Owl since it is especially prone to rapid waterlogging. It is known for example, that Barn Owls will not hunt at all in heavy rain (Mikkola 1983) and Tawny Owls, too, experience much lower capture rates (Hirons 1985). In addition, the activity of some small mammals is inhibited during periods of very wet weather (Churchfield 1986; Flowerdew 1984) and the acoustical clues normally provided to the hunting Barn Owl are likely to become suppressed on saturated leaf litter, making prey once again more difficult to locate. The inability of the Barn Owl to catch sufficient food is likely to influence overall breeding success in a number of ways.

Sustained rainfall, like prolonged snowcover, can contribute to breeding failure by reducing the chances of egg fertilisation, preventing egg-laying altogether or delaying it for a number of weeks, leading to late fledging and poor survival. In addition, food shortages later in the breeding season, during incubation and early brooding, can encourage the female to move off eggs or young resulting in chilling and nest failure. During the fledging period too, insufficient food can lead to the starvation of young, with the result that overall breeding success is reduced. Cannibalism of young has previously been associated with heavy rainfall and the inadequate provision of prey (Baudvin in Bunn *et al* 1982).

Cannibalism also occurs commonly (and sometimes simultaneously) with captive Barn Owls which are not subject to food shortage. There is an indication that although heavy rainfall may indeed be associated with this phenomenon, the actual trigger may be high atmospheric pressure associated with electrical storms (Brice, Shawyer unpublished observations). The stress brought on by this type of extreme weather may well explain the simultaneous occurrence of cannibalism in both captive and free-living populations.

Drought

Unlike the previous climatic extreme, drought does not influence the hunting ability of the Barn Owl but can act directly by reducing vole abundance. Previous studies of several small rodents have shown that microtines were the least able to survive drought (Lindeborg in Bunn *et al* 1982). A rapid dying off or sudden retardation of grass growth during long periods of summer drought results in the inability of the vole to provide sufficient food to its developing young and to meet adult needs. As a consequence, a crash in vole numbers can occur (Bunn *et al* 1982). Possibly only the most severe of summer droughts in Britain can reduce prey numbers to the extent where Barn Owls (especially during the late stages of fledging) experience high mortality. Unlike the effects of heavy snow and summer rainfall, drought acts later in the season drastically reducing the numbers of young birds available to breed the following year.

Climatic extremes in the British Isles are believed therefore to influence the annual population trends of the Barn Owl not specifically through an increase in direct mortality but primarily as a result of reducing the species' breeding success.

SOURCE MATERIALS AND METHODS

Estimates of Annual Population Trends

A measure of the relative annual abundance of the Barn Owl in the British Isles has been based on data supplied to the Ringing Scheme of the British Trust for Ornithology by experienced ornithologists since 1909. These records were originally categorised in terms of the total number of Barn Owls ringed in any one year together with those specimens annually recorded dead. After 1931, the birds which were ringed were differentiated into two categories representing both adults and pulli. The number of young owlets ringed provides direct information about the annual breeding success of this species and because the records are representative of the country as a whole, it also provides an excellent indication of the Barn Owl's relative annual abundance.

Interpretation of the ringing data can be considered problematic for many species, mainly because of the inconsistencies which arise from variations in human ringing effort from one year to the next. Population trends for individual species are therefore more commonly expressed, not in terms of the absolute number of pulli ringed, but as a percentage of the total pulli of all species for each relevant year (expressed as an index). In contrast to many other bird families, Barn Owls and birds of prey in general, lend themselves particularly well to this sort of analysis since their fidelity to traditional sites, year after year, allows a more consistent pattern of annual ringing to emerge (Spencer and Hudson 1982).

In those years when a specific increase in Barn Owl ringing intensity has occurred, it is well-documented (Mead and Hudson 1984; Spencer 1968). The first increase occurred in 1967 and the second around 1980, both accounting for the sustained upward shifts evident in those years.

The ringing totals for pulli and adults were first differentiated in the statistics in 1932 and it is records from 1932 onwards which have been used to analyse population changes (Figure 3). Whilst these cyclical fluctuations can be safely interpreted in terms of the years of peak maxima and minima, the magnitude of these individual fluctuations require more cautious interpretation. Between 1941 and 1947 however, a major increase in Barn Owl abundance emerged, undoubtedly reflecting the relaxation of persecution pressure during the years of the Second World War.

Climatic Research

In the British Isles, the regional variations in climate, especially those involving snowfall and rainfall, are often considerable. The southern and western seaboards usually suffer less than the rest of the country from sustained winter snowfall whilst experiencing, along with Ireland, a much heavier annual rainfall. The meteorological data used for this comparative study of the influence of climate on Barn Owl numbers were therefore extracted from a representative sample of relatively low lying meteorological stations throughout the British Isles, relevant to the species' known distribution.

Climatic data were obtained with the kind assistance of the Meteorological Office, Bracknell. Statistics of snow at twenty geographically separated meteorological stations in the British Isles were derived from the Monthly Weather Reports in which values were expressed in terms of snow depth and number of days snow lying. Snow duration means from twenty stations were thus charted for individual years from 1947-1973 at five ranges of depth from 0-2 cm to 16-20 cm. The years at which snowcover was maximal remained unaffected by the depth selected for this analysis and the cyclical pattern which emerged also remained unchanged.

The number of days snow lying has therefore been taken as that defined by the Meteorological Office as depths above zero centimetres where snow covers one half or more of the ground surrounding the observation station at 09.00 GMT. The material used to construct a homogeneous set of annual snow data from 1947 to 1986 was selected from the records of eight meteorological stations from geographically distributed regions of Britain (Meteorological Office 1985) and from the Monthly Weather Reports of the same stations, or those closely matched for region and height, for the earlier years from 1915-1946.

Although snow duration figures were first recorded at a few locations as early as 1912, the differences in situation of many of these stations precluded strict comparison with the 1915-1986 figures. Where gaps arose in the snow data prior to 1915, snow lying was determined from a combined analysis of weekly precipitation levels and the corresponding daily air temperatures. Confirmation of the relative intensity of snowcover for each of these fourteen winters was derived from the classification system used by Bonacina (1927, 1936) for grading annual snow severity.

Although the number of days of lying snow in any single winter does not imply that it has lain continuously over this period, it provides a reliable comparative index of the intensity of annual snow cover. It can however be shown from a study of the Daily Weather Reports that the number of days continuous snowcover which is experienced in any one winter, is generally about half that of the calculated yearly figure for most low-lying meteorological stations below 150 m. For example, when the winter total is given as 20 days, snowcover can be considered to have lain continuously over a minimum period of 10 of these days. Annual snowcover is shown in Figure 3.

Spells of continuous and heavy rainfall can influence Barn Owl breeding success from the period of egg-laying in early May through to fledging in September. With this in mind, summer rainfall totals were computed for this study by the Meteorological Office from the monthly rainfall figures recorded for England and Wales from 1727. Only the most severe rainfall seasons since 1901 have been taken and included in Figure 3 where the rainfall excess was greater than 140% of the 1901-1986 annual mean.

Rainfall deficiency, or drought, unlike rainfall excess is more of a late summer phenomenon and as such can exert its major effect on fledging survival during a more advanced stage of the breeding season. Drought acts through its influence on grass growth by reducing vole numbers at a time during fledging which would under normal conditions represent a period of rapidly increasing vole abundance.

Generally, meteorological examinations of drought intensity are conducted in terms of the departure from the average annual rainfall condition. The period June to August was selected for assessing drought severity as the months best representative of exerting maximum impact on Barn Owl breeding success. These data, and the recommendations for assessing drought in the context of this research, were again kindly provided by the Meteorological Office. As recommended, only those years where the rainfall deficiency is more than 40% below the average were accepted as representative of a severe drought season.

Unlike the data collected on Barn Owl abundance, there have been few long term studies of annual vole density in Britain. The information shown in Figure 3 concerning vole population peaks and troughs has therefore been collated from a number of short-term investigations reported in the literature (Snow 1968; Picozzi and Hewson 1970; Southern 1970; Mitchell *et al* 1974; Charles 1981; Taylor 1984; Richards 1985; and Petty 1987).

All information relating to the movement of Barn Owls following climatic extremes has been obtained from an intensive literature search of books and papers published since the turn of the century.

RESULTS

Population Decline in Years of Climatic Extreme

The temporary rise and fall in Barn Owl numbers over the fifty-five year period between 1931 and 1986 is represented by sixteen fluctuations showing a mean frequency of 3.4 years. The snow lying data for the same period demonstrate a remarkably similar cyclical pattern, with a mean frequency of 3.4 years over a range of sixteen full cycles. So close is the correlation between the years of minimal Barn Owl abundance and the years of maximal snow duration that twelve of the sixteen cycles over this fifty-five year period demonstrate a precise correlation and the cycles appear as mirror images.

In those years when winter snowcover reached or exceeded 20 days duration, an immediate crash in the Barn Owl population followed, as measured by the species' subsequent breeding productivity. Even small increases in snow duration above the 17 days seasonal mean (1901-1986) appear to be responsible for causing a noticeable decline in numbers.

Figure 3 illustrates the relative severity of each winter in terms of days snow lying, with the particularly harsh winters of 1946/47 and 1962/63 being the snowiest since 1814 (Ticehurst 1948). Snow duration data prior to 1931 have been presented here to highlight the long run of snow-free winters which occurred from 1901-1939; the implications of which are discussed in relation to the long-term decline of this species in Part III of this report.

Unlike snow duration, excess rainfall (shown in Figure 3) shows no cyclical tendency, with only five of these climatic extremes having occurred since 1901. The negative influence of sustained and heavy rainfall on Barn Owl numbers is dramatically illustrated in 1958. This was the wettest May to September season since 1879, and the only year in ringing history when productivity was so low that no Barn Owl pulli were ringed, suggesting a severe crash in the overall population. Since the early 1930s only one other severe rainfall year has occurred – in 1946. This year is also represented by a marked decline in Barn Owl numbers. Summer (May to September) rainfall excesses greater than 140% of the 1901–1986 mean appear capable of causing a major reduction in the species' breeding potential and subsequent population level.

Drought, which for the purpose of this paper is described as rainfall deficiency, again shows no regular frequency although four periods of major summer (June to August) droughts have occurred since 1901. These are shown in Figure 3.

The effects of drought, unlike the previous two types of climatic extreme, are not always fully reflected in the ringing totals of the drought year itself, but are often indicated by further reduced totals the following year. This arises because summer droughts exert their maximal effect on plant growth, vole reproduction and hence owl fledging survival, in the months of July and August after the majority of Barn Owl pulli have already been ringed. The lowered ringing totals which are often apparent in the year subsequent to the drought year reflect, therefore, the abnormally high losses through starvation of juvenile birds which in times of more normal prey abundance would have thrived to become breeding adults. The negative impact of the severe droughts of 1949 and 1976 on the Barn Owl population was therefore further reflected in the crashes of 1950 and 1977.

The severity of these two droughts is demonstrated by the fact that 1976 was the driest summer since 1766. Dairy farmers were faced with grassless pastures as early as July in England and Wales, although Scotland was much more fortunate (Mortimer 1976). Similiar conditions prevailed in 1949, the third driest summer since 1887. The nationwide drought of 1983, unlike those of 1976 and 1949, was uncharacteristically preceded by a very wet spring. The residual moisture content of the ground in that summer was therefore sufficient to maintain good grass yields in most areas (Marsh and Lees 1986). This was also undoubtedly the factor responsible for maintaining vole survival in 1983 and for the drought's less pronounced impact on the Barn Owl population in that year. Annual rainfall deficiencies more than 40% below the 1901–1986 mean are indicative of a major crash in the Barn Owl population as demonstrated by the species' low abundance during the summer of the drought year itself, or in the subsequent breeding season.

Since 1931, there have been a total of seventeen occurrences when Barn Owl numbers have declined to a major low. In fifteen (88%) of these instances, a precise correlation exists with those years demonstrating a climatic extreme (Table 1). Whilst the same correlation may also be true for the two additional occurrences between 1939 and 1945, the overwhelming increase in the population caused by the relaxation of persecution during the years of the Second World War preclude any comparative cyclical interpretation.

In contrast to the recording system used for monitoring Barn Owl numbers, small mammal fluctuations have not been subject to the same amount of prolonged or consistent study. The data which do exist tend therefore to be limited (especially over the period 1940–1960), and geographically fragmented. Nevertheless, by combining the results of those studies which have been conducted it can be seen from Figure 3 that the cyclical decline in Short-tailed Vole numbers are in step with those of the Barn Owl.

Severe climatic events also appear to be capable of inducing nomadic movements of Barn Owls out of regions where prey has temporarily been depleted. These movements can be extensive. During the severe winter of 1982, three individual reports of large scale movements of Barn Owls were reported, involving in excess of nine birds in each group. A large party observed on a direct flight from the eastern borders of Nottinghamshire was reported in Norfolk the same day. Nomadic movement of up to eleven individuals was also observed on direct flight westwards from Warwickshire and in Ireland a large communal roost was found in January of the same year.

A search of the historical literature reveals that sudden influxes of Barn Owls have occurred in years associated with a major climatic event. In Glamorgan, there was, apparently, an extraordinary invasion in the winter of 1949/1950 following the severe drought of the previous summer. During the next few years breeding was noted in a number of places from which Barn Owls had previously been absent (Heathcote et al 1967). A remarkable immigration also occurred in Cornwall during the same winter followed by some mortality due to starvation (Penhallerick 1978). Similar reports of mass local influxes were reported from Huntingdonshire and Lancashire at a time when the overall population elsewhere in Britain was in a state of noticeable decline (Tebbett 1967; Oakes 1953).

Although there is little suggestion that any of these birds were of continental origin or that these movements were on the scale of those frequently observed in Europe, climatic extremes appear to have the potential for inducing a sudden redistribution of an otherwise sedentary population into regions where the species had previously been uncommon.

Mild Winters

Whilst severe climatic conditions can exert a negative influence on Barn Owl breeding success, mild winters which can induce year-long reproduction in some small mammals (Smyth 1966), can in turn encourage high fledging success rates and multiple-brooding in Barn Owls.

Two and rarely three broods can be produced under these conditions. Although this now appears a much less common event in Britain than has been suggested in the past, fifteen cases of double-brooding and two cases of triple-brooding were notified between 1982-1986. Nine of these events occurred in the breeding season of 1984. This was notably in a year when there was little winter snow and average spring/summer rainfall. Vole populations were correspondingly high and the Barn Owl's overall breeding success, as measured from the ringing figures, was the best for many years. These reports of multiple-brooding were almost exclusively confined to the counties of the western seaboard (where the winters are generally the mildest in Britain), from Cornwall, Devon, Somerset and Anglesey through to Wigtown-

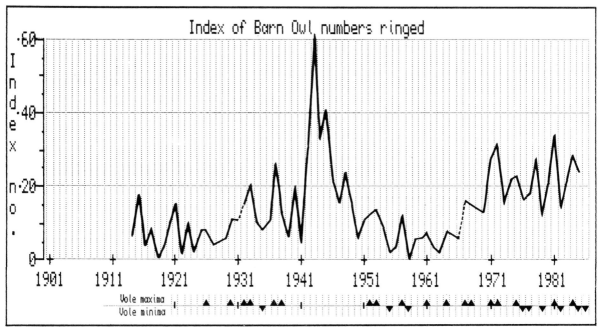

Index of Barn Owl numbers ringed

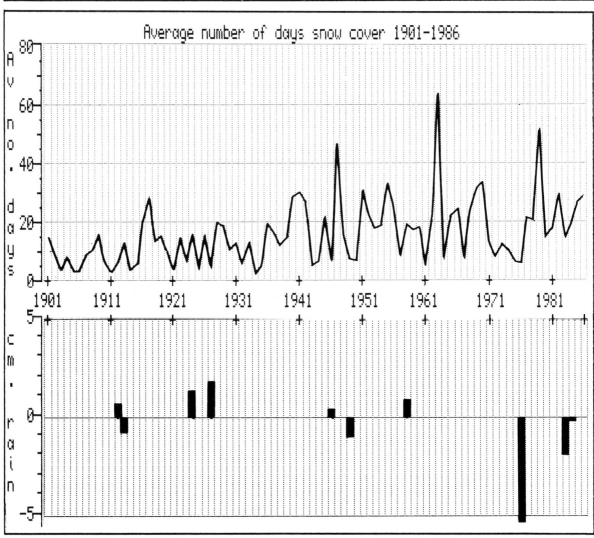

Average number of days snow cover 1901-1986

Fig. 3 **The influence of climatic extremes and vole abundance on the cyclical changes in the Barn Owl population.**

An index showing the annual fluctuations in Barn Owl numbers.
This index is derived from the number of young Barn Owls ringed annually in the British Isles as a percentage of the annual totals of ringed nestlings of all species.

◄

Vole abundance.
Vole maxima and minima have been derived from a series of small mammal population studies conducted since 1926 and reported in the literature. (For references see text).

◄

Duration of winter snowcover.
Compiled from data included in the Monthly Weather Reports and Snow Survey of Great Britain (Met. Office 1985), for low-lying meteorological stations in the British Isles 1901–1986.

◄

Excess summer rainfall
Years in which May–September rainfall exceeded 140% of the annual average 1901–1986 (35.6 cm).

◄

Drought
Years in which June–August rainfall showed a deficit of more than 40% of the annual average 1901–1986 (21.6 cm). (Rainfall data compiled from the monthly rainfall statistics for all meteorological stations in England and Wales).

TABLE 1

Summary showing the correlation between years of minimal Barn Owl population and years of climatic extremes 1931–1986

Years of minimal Barn Owl productivity	Barn Owl cycle frequency	Years of maximal snow cover	Years of maximal summer rainfall	Years of major summer drought
1931		1931		
		1933		
1935/6	4	1936		
1939	4			
1941	2	1941		
1944	3			
		1945	1946	
1947	3	1947		
1950	3			1949
		1951		
1955	5	1955		
1958	3	1958	1958	
1963	5	1963		
1966	3	1966		
1970	4	1970		
1973	3	1973		
1976/7	3			1976
1979	3	1979		
1982	3	1982		
1986	4	1986		

(War Years)

mean **3.4**

shire and Kirkcudbrightshire.

The overall results of this study indicate that extreme climatic conditions are the underlying factor responsible for regulating the cyclic fluctuations in the Barn Owl population in Britain. Prolonged snow duration, continuous rainfall and drought all appear to act on the Barn Owl by inhibiting (or delaying) optimal fertilisation, egg production and fledging success, as a direct result of a major reduction in the numbers and availability of its small mammal prey.

DISCUSSION

There have been a number of previous studies linking the numbers of avian predators with the relative abundance of their prey (Bunn *et al* 1982). These studies have involved birds of prey which select the Short-tailed Vole as their major source of food (Lockie 1955; Galushin 1974; Baudvin 1975; Newton 1979; Village 1981, 1986). Very few long-term studies have however been conducted in the British Isles which provide any annual measure of vole abundance – making any direct correlations of this type less precise. Those studies of small mammal abundance which have been undertaken, although generally restricted to areas of commercial forest, nevertheless now suggest that the years of minimal vole and Barn Owl abundance are coincident.

The rhythmical changes in small mammal populations have since the classic work by Elton in 1942 attracted much interest and many theories have been advanced as to the primary factors responsible for this cycling phenomenon. These theories have emphasised various factors such as reduced food supply, predation, parasitism, social behaviour, stress and genetics.

The cycling of small mammals has been shown to be synchronous not only throughout widely separated communities over extensive regions, but can also simultaneously involve differing species. (Galushin 1974). This suggests that the factor or factors responsible for this phenomenon prevail over large areas.

The 3-4 year abundance rhythm which has been described for microtines throughout the temperate and arctic regions of Europe, Asia and North America is less common in the more stable climates of the tropics and Southern Hemisphere.

There have been no systematic studies in Britain which have attempted to assess the impact of climate on Barn Owl numbers. This study has however now demonstrated that climate appears to be the major cause of these cyclical population changes and is the ultimate trigger governing the abundance of the Barn Owl through its principal prey, the Short-tailed Vole.

Muirhead (1889-1895) was probably the first ornithological writer to ascribe the Barn Owl's decline to the effects of severe winter weather, whilst Ticehurst and Hartley (1948) specifically identified the persistence of snowcover as the most relevant of the winter variables. Prolonged periods of winter snow not only reduce the ability of the Barn Owl to find food as vole activity becomes suppressed and disguised under the snow blanket, but also now appears capable of having a more direct effect in reducing the density of the over-wintering vole population.

As well as the increased difficulties to the vole in maintaining and defending the more restricted foraging grounds and rapidly diminishing food caches under snow, temperatures below 0°C have been shown to cause high additional mortality to small mammals acutely stressed by food shortage (Howard in Bunn *et al* 1982). It is also known that following harsh winters, female voles, invariably in poor condition, seem incapable of gaining sufficient weight and have major difficulties in raising young. The young themselves show heavy mortality, resulting in an abnormally slow population build-up in that particular year (Frank 1957). Heavy rains and drought conditions have also been described as detrimental to vole survival (Bunn *et al* 1982; Baudvin 1975).

In Britain the difference between years of low and high vole abundance can be so great that numbers can vary in optimal habitats of extensive unmanaged, ungrazed grasslands from between 5 – 1000 voles per ha. Exceptionally, dense populations of around 3000 per ha can occur during peak densities of the type witnessed in young forestry plantations in central Scotland in the late summers of 1952/53 (Charles 1981). Not surprisingly, vole numbers along with those of the Barn Owl appear to fluctuate with much greater amplitude on the hills and downlands of the British Isles where the most extreme snowfall and rainfall events occur.

The other major prey species of the Barn Owl in the British Isles, the Common Shrew *Sorex auraneus*, Wood Mouse *Apodemus sylvaticus* and Bank Vole *Clethrionomys glareolus*, may also decline in step with the Short-tailed Vole and indeed this has been shown for shrews and voles in northern Finland. However, although both the carnivorous shrew and herbivorous voles show classic 3-4 year cyclical fluctuations in Scandinavia, like the Wood Mouse, little true cyclical tendency has so far been demonstrated in Britain (Gipps *et al* 1986). In those years where a serious scarcity in the numbers of these species has previously been identified, they are nevertheless coincident with the troughs in Barn Owl abundance (Southern 1959).

During periods of major vole decline, Barn Owl breeding numbers appear more stable in habitats which generally maintain higher shrew densities or where diverse habitats provide a varied choice of prey.

The cyclical decline of the vole, and in turn that of the Barn Owl, the subject of this study, appears to be significantly influenced by the occurrence of sudden climatic events such as heavy rainfall, drought and in particular prolonged annual snowcover of 20 days or more.

SUMMARY

The Barn Owl population in the British Isles is known for its short-term fluctuations. These annual fluctuations have previously been linked to the rhythmical changes in the cyclic availability of the Short-tailed Vole, the major prey species of the Barn Owl on the mainland in England, Wales and Scotland.

This study has identified that the Barn Owl population has, since earliest records, shown remarkably rhythmical fluctuations in numbers with a mean frequency of 3.4 years. A close examination of the meteorological data since 1901 has shown that the species has consistently declined to its lowest temporary abundance following winters of peak snowcover and that this has been evident since reliable records of Barn Owl numbers first became available in 1932.

More remarkable however, has been the discovery that the years corresponding to maximal snow duration have themselves consistently cycled with a frequency of 3.4 years in line with the troughs in Barn Owl numbers.

Whilst Barn Owl population levels have been well-documented annually for over fifty years, much less information exists about the periodic changes in vole abundance in Britain. The information which is available however, further confirms that the years of minimal Barn Owl numbers are coincident with the troughs in vole abundance. Indeed it is reported that vole cycle workers elsewhere have demonstrated a periodicity of 3.3 years (Frank 1957), almost identical to that which has now been established for the Barn Owl.

Snow duration appears, therefore, to be the underlying factor responsible for these cyclical, and hence temporary fluctuations in Barn Owl numbers by regulating the overall abundance or availability of prey and thereby influencing the bird's reproductive success. The population 'crashes' which have been experienced since 1932 can be identified with those winters demonstrating 20 days or more snowcover. It is probable that an increased level of mortality only occurs in those situations where annual snowcover exceeds 35 days.

Comparative analysis of the Barn Owl population data and meteorological records further demonstrates that other climatic extremes, such as excessive summer rainfall and drought, although of an infrequent and non-cyclical occurrence, can also induce a decline in the Barn Owl population. The failure of the male to provide the female with sufficient food during periods of excessive rainfall in early summer can lead to a high incidence of infertile clutches. When heavy rainfall occurs later in the year, this can result in the starvation of young. In a similar way, drought can suddenly reduce small mammal numbers to the extent where fledgling mortality becomes high in late summer.

A seasonal rainfall excess greater than 140% of the annual mean, and rainfall deficiencies more than 40% below this average, have consistently caused major crashes in numbers as a result of poor overall breeding success.

The onset of the Barn Owl's long-term decline this century has commonly been associated with specific years by most contemporary writers. Likewise, the causes of the bird's demise have often been linked with the human and environmental factors which began operating at that time. The results of this research would suggest that the so-called origins of the long-term decline need more considered interpretation since they can invariably be traced to a year when a major climatic event occurred, reflecting simply the beginnings of a temporary population crash caused by natural factors.

Climatic extremes, in particular snow duration and drought, also appear capable of stimulating mass nomadic movements of Barn Owls with the result that colonisation and subsequent breeding can be shifted into regions where the species had previously been much less common.

This research strongly indicates that these three climatic extremes predominantly govern the population level in Britain by inhibiting the Barn Owl's reproductive potential through a reduced food supply, as opposed to directly reducing numbers through a major increase in adult mortality.

PART III –
THE PRESENT

THE CURRENT POPULATION LEVEL IN THE BRITISH ISLES

Parts I and II of this report have dealt with the status of the Barn Owl in the British Isles up to the beginning of the present *Survey*, together with the climatic factors which control the short term fluctuations in population. They establish a historical and scientific basis for an analysis of this *Survey's* findings and an interpretation of the factors responsible for the Barn Owl's long-term decline.

This part describes in detail the results of the Barn Owl Survey of Britain and Ireland which was conducted over a period of four years following the breeding season in 1982 until the end of 1985. (The aims of the work and the methods used to conduct the *Survey* are given in Appendix II).

The Barn Owl remains widely distributed in non-urban areas throughout most of the British Isles with the exception of the northern half of Scotland where it becomes much more scattered. It was found to be present in 50% of the 10-km squares in the British Isles and breeding was confirmed in 81% of these. Numbers are rather sparse and localised throughout, but in a few areas the Barn Owl can still be considered very common ranging between 10-30 pairs per 100 km².

The *Survey* has established a total population in England and Wales of 3,750 pairs with an additional 650 pairs in Scotland.

In the Channel Islands, the current population falls within the range 32–46 pairs (Jersey 12-17, Guernsey 12–16, Sark 3–5, Alderney 5-8). Whilst in 1951 it was noted that one-third of the Island population of Jersey was of the dark *guttata* form, this sub-species is now only rarely observed on either Jersey or Guernsey.

In Ireland, the lack of observers has restricted adequate coverage. The population has therefore been approximated at between 600-900 pairs based on an estimate taken from four well-covered sample areas, of a probable average of 2-3 pairs of Barn Owls for each of the 10-km squares found occupied in Ireland during the breeding seasons of 1982-1985.

In 1932, Blaker recorded the population in England and Wales at 12,000 pairs which, on the basis of the present data, indicates a 69% decline during the last fifty years. Whilst numbers in both Scotland and Ireland have undoubtedly shown a significant decline over the same period, the lack of any past numerical data prevents any precise estimation to be made about the extent of the decrease.

Population levels are presented on the basis of the Barn Owl's abundance in each 10-km square in England, Wales and Scotland (Map 5). In addition, levels are shown in terms of Vice-county totals (Table 2). Following careful interpretation of the data generated from the Census in 1932, abundance has been translated into 10-km squares to allow direct comparisons to be made of the changes which have taken place over this fifty-year period at both the local and county level (Maps 4 & 8. Table 2).

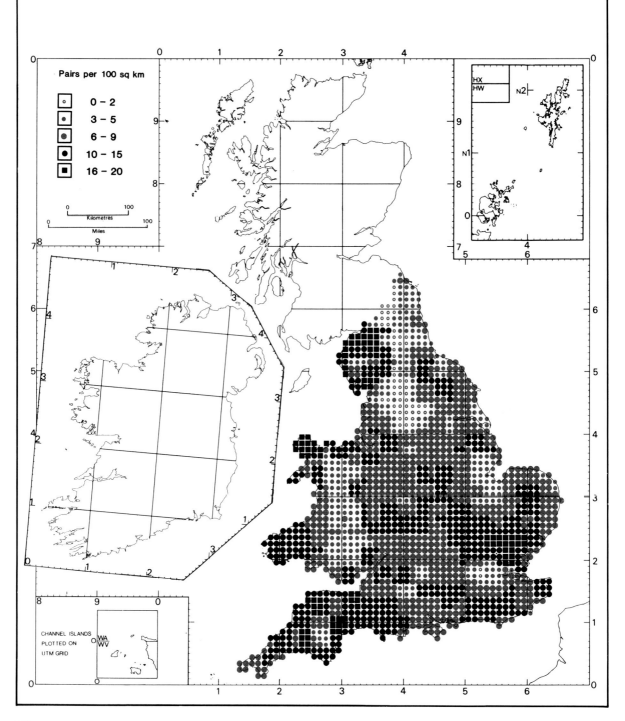

Map 4 **The breeding density and distribution of the Barn Owl in England and Wales in 1932.**

(Re-drawn from Blaker, 1934 on the basis of 10 km squares).

Pairs per 100 sq km

- 0 – 2
- 3 – 5
- 6 – 9
- 10 – 15
- 16 – 20

Kilometres

Miles

CHANNEL ISLANDS
PLOTTED ON
UTM GRID

WA
WV

Map 5 ***The breeding density and distribution of the Barn Owl in the British Isles 1982–1985.***

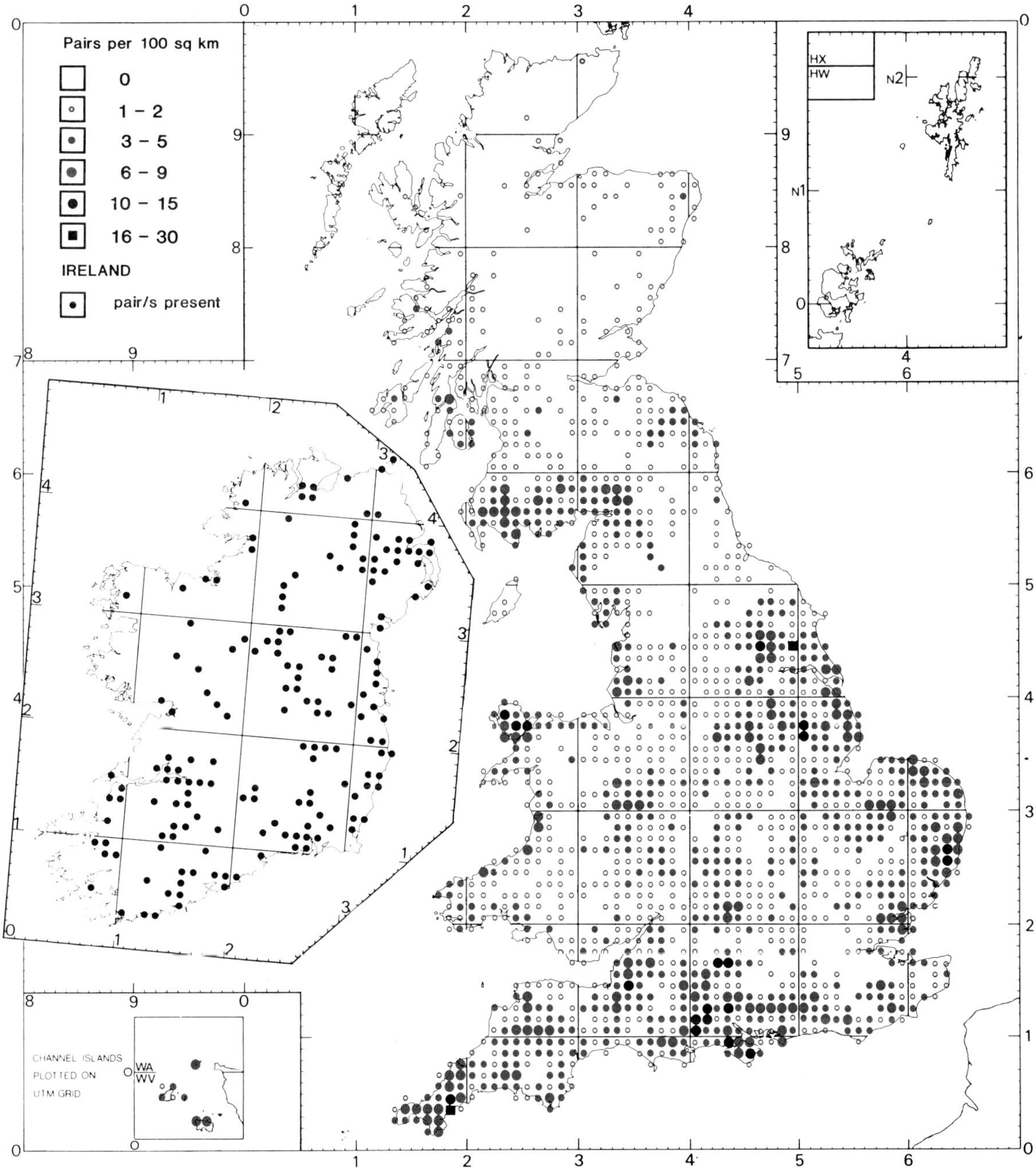

Pairs per 100 sq km
0
1 - 2
3 - 5
6 - 9
10 - 15
16 - 30
IRELAND
pair/s present
CHANNEL ISLANDS
PLOTTED ON
UTM GRID
WA
WV
HX
HW
N2
N1

TABLE 2 **Vice-County Population Estimates 1932–85 and Current Status**

		1932		1982–85		%	Status
		Total Pairs	Pairs/ 100 sq km	Total Pairs	Pairs/ 100 sq km	Change	see footnote
001	Cornwall W	103	8.3	124	10.0	+20	
002	Cornwall E	239	10.3	145	6.2	−39	
003	Devon S	381	10.5	114	3.1	−70	★
004	Devon N	331	10.7	121	3.9	−63	★
005	Somerset S	208	10.4	61	3.1	−71	★
006	Somerset N	178	8.2	95	4.3	−47	
007	Wilts N	128	8.3	24	1.6	−81	★★
008	Wilts S	128	6.6	90	4.6	−30	
009	Dorset	275	10.9	112	4.4	−59	
010	Isle of Wight	29	7.6	51	13.4	+76	
011	Hants S	150	7.6	104	5.3	−31	
012	Hants N	201	10.4	40	2.1	−80	★★
013	Sussex W	186	10.5	75	4.2	−60	
014	Sussex E	216	10.8	63	3.2	−71	★
015	Kent E	220	9.4	67	2.9	−70	★
016	Kent W	100	7.2	23	1.7	−77	★★
017	Surrey	137	8.1	34	2.0	−75	★★
018	Essex S	137	9.4	58	4.0	−58	★
019	Essex N	332	15.0	62	2.8	−81	★
020	Herts	210	12.9	9	0.6	−96	★★
021	Middlesex	30	4.5	2	0.3	−93	★★
022	Berks	119	6.3	38	2.0	−68	★★
023	Oxford	130	6.7	45	2.3	−65	★★
024	Bucks	160	8.3	19	1.0	−88	★★
025	Suffolk E	159	7.4	117	5.4	−26	
026	Suffolk W	188	11.2	32	1.9	−83	★★
027	Norfolk E	202	8.2	109	4.4	−46	
028	Norfolk W	240	8.4	82	2.9	−66	★
029	Cambridge	144	6.7	34	1.6	−76	★★
030	Bedford	140	11.3	29	2.3	−79	★★
031	Hunts	69	5.5	12	1.0	−83	★★
032	Northampton	249	10.5	48	2.0	−81	★★
033	Gloucester E	111	6.5	35	2.0	−68	★★
034	Gloucester W	112	7.2	34	2.2	−70	★★
035	Monmouth	120	8.6	25	1.8	−79	★★
036	Hereford	192	8.8	48	2.2	−75	★★
037	Worcester	184	10.1	32	1.8	−83	★★
038	Warwick	237	9.4	58	2.3	−76	★★
039	Stafford	210	7.0	44	1.5	−79	★★
040	Salop	287	8.2	95	2.7	−67	★
041	Glamorgan	105	5.0	36	1.7	−66	★★
042	Brecon	70	3.9	17	0.9	−76	★★
043	Radnor	48	3.9	12	1.0	−75	★★
044	Carmarthen	187	7.9	34	1.4	−82	★★
045	Pembroke	210	13.2	55	3.5	−74	★
046	Cardigan	138	7.7	78	4.3	−43	
047	Montgomery	93	4.5	20	1.0	−78	★★
048	Merioneth	60	3.5	30	1.8	−50	★★
049	Caernarvon	90	6.1	47	3.2	−48	★
050	Denbigh	109	6.3	24	1.4	−78	★★
051	Flint	60	9.1	16	2.4	−73	★★
052	Anglesey	126	17.6	68	9.5	−46	
053	Lincoln S	177	6.3	61	2.2	−66	★★
054	Lincoln N	332	8.1	140	3.4	−58	★
055	Leic & Rutland	243	9.5	26	1.0	−89	★★
056	Notts	208	9.5	97	4.4	−53	
057	Derby	245	9.5	41	1.6	−83	★★
058	Cheshire	239	9.1	33	1.3	−86	★★

		1932		1982–85		%	Status
		Total Pairs	Pairs/ 100 sq km	Total Pairs	Pairs/ 100 sq km	Change	see footnote
059	Lancs S	186	6.3	55	1.9	−70	★★
060	Lancs W	78	6.1	28	2.2	−64	★★
061	S E York	188	6.3	125	4.2	−34	
062	N E York	300	9.0	50	1.5	−83	★★
063	S W York	199	5.8	48	1.4	−76	★★
064	Mid W York	120	3.4	30	0.8	−75	★★
065	N W York	112	4.5	7	0.3	−94	★★
066	Durham	153	5.8	18	0.7	−88	★★
067	Northumb S	98	2.8	24	0.7	−76	★★
068	Cheviotland	52	3.0	25	1.4	−52	★★
069	Wmlnd & N Lancs	270	10.1	42	1.6	−84	★★
070	Cumberland	474	12.0	77	2.0	−84	★★
071	Isle of Man			4	0.7		★★
072	Dumfries			94	3.4		★
073	Kirkcudbright			85	3.7		★
074	Wigtown			73	5.8		
075	Ayr			39	1.3		★★
076	Renfrew			5	0.9		★★
077	Lanark			14	0.6		★★
078	Peebles			9	1.0		★★
079	Selkirk			5	0.7		★★
080	Roxburgh			26	1.5		★★
081	Berwick			32	2.7		★
082	Haddington			10	1.4		★★
083	Edinburgh			11	1.4		★★
084	Linlithgow			3	1.0		★★
085	Fife			14	0.9		★★
086	Stirling			7	0.6		★★
087	West Perth			7	0.5		★★
088	Mid Perth			10	0.3		★★
089	East Perth			4	0.2		★★
090	Forfar			7	0.3		★★
091	Kincardine			3	0.3		★★
092	South Aberdeen &			28	0.6		★★
093	North Aberdeen						
094	Banff			5	0.3		★★
095	Elgin			9	0.7		★★
096	Easterness &			25	0.2		★★
097	Westerness & 104						
098	Main Argyll & 101, 102, 103			74	0.9		★★
099	Dunbarton			10	1.6		★★
100	Clyde Isles			16	2.8		★
101	Kintyre						
102	South Ebudes						
103	Mid Ebudes						
104	North Ebudes						
105	West Ross &			10	0.1		★★
106	East Ross						
107	East Sutherland			4			★★
108	West Sutherland						
109	Caithness			1			★★
110	Outer Hebrides						
111	Orkney						
112	Zetland						
England & Wales		12142		3778		−69	
England, Wales & Scotland				4418			
Channel Islands				39			

Status: ★★ **Critical** 0–2.5 pairs/100 sq km.   ★ **Vulnerable** 2.6–4.0 pairs/100 sq km.

The overall population figure for the British Isles of 5,000 pairs cannot be considered synonymous with the number of pairs which breed annually. Failure to begin breeding during some seasons is not uncommon with this species and as we have previously seen, ringing records suggest that the entire population may fail in years when climatic extremes occur and prey numbers are low. The marked annual variability in breeding success and the fluctuations in overall population which can result, emphasise the importance of conducting a nationwide survey such as this over a period of at least 3-4 years (one vole cycle), if meaningful population figures are to be obtained.

The number of additional unpaired Barn Owls present in the current population is difficult to determine. However, the presence of a high proportion of unmated birds was a recurrent theme from many observers throughout this *Survey*. Indications from the many regions which were sampled over this four-year period were that the number of singletons present in an average year may vary from 10% of the total population, in regions of high abundance, to 40% in areas where breeding numbers are low. Assuming the overall figure lies somewhere between these two extremes, the number of unmated individuals is probably in the order of 1,250 compared with the 1,000 single birds suggested by Blaker in 1932. Today, the higher percentage of unpaired Barn Owls, indicated from these figures, is undoubtedly the result of the bird's more fragmented distribution throughout much of the British Isles as a result of habitat isolation and restricted dispersal possibilities, all of which reduce the opportunity of finding suitable mates.

HABITAT SELECTION

Habitat selection has been considered here in terms of the major factors which determine the selection of foraging grounds and those influencing the choice of nest site. Clearly both of these are intimately linked, for even in situations where there is a surplus of nesting sites, habitats will only be occupied if prey are also freely available. As such, only rarely are the major hunting grounds more than 1 km from the selected nest site, exceptions usually occurring only where the food supply is more strictly confined within linear grasslands of the type present, for example, on the open fenland drains or around the perimeter of woodlands, where the birds can range as far as 3 km from the breeding site.

The selection of habitat in the British Isles is largely determined by the influence of climate, notably the duration of snowcover. Rainfall on the other hand, appears to govern the choice of nesting site within this chosen habitat. The fact that climate plays an important role should not perhaps be surprising since this report has already demonstrated that climatic extremes seriously influence the breeding biology of this species and, as will be shown later, have contributed to its long-term decline.

The Influence of Altitude

In regional terms, the duration of snowcover varies considerably throughout the British Isles. In the regions of high ground in most of Wales and in central and northern Britain where snowcover annually exceeds 20

days, the Barn Owl is a very rare breeding bird. Even in the lowlands throughout much of eastern England where snowcover averages 15 or more days per annum, the species remains uncommon. Low population levels also occur in areas of central and southern England where land exceeds 100 m above sea level and where once again the number of days of lying snow annually averages 15 or more days (Maps 9 and 11). In terms of altitude, 100 m can therefore be considered to be close to the upper limit of habitat suitability for this species with only 18% of the population in the British Isles currently breeding above this height and less than 7% in excess of 150 m (Figure 4).

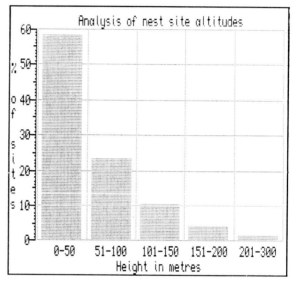

Fig. 4 **Height above mean sea level of 2,699 Barn Owl nest sites in the British Isles expressed as a percentage of all known sites 1982–1985.** *Sites over 300 m formed less than 1% of the total.*

This altitude limit however, extends to over 150 m in south-western and extreme western counties (where much of the land is of greater altitude anyway). This can be tolerated only because of the mild maritime influences which result in January temperatures 3 °C higher, and annual snow duration shorter by 10 or more days, than that found elsewhere in the British Isles. It can thus be concluded that 'upland' populations, where they exist, must today be regarded as very marginal and therefore subject to rapid decline following harsh winters or longer periods of worsening climate.

The Optimum Habitat Type

On a more localised basis this survey has found substantial variability in the type of habitat utilised by the Barn Owl for foraging. Whilst traditional mixed and open farmland is preferred where small meadows and hedgerow provide the hunting areas, notable exceptions occur. It was a careful analysis of these lesser known Barn Owl habitats that has allowed identification of the specific features within these habitats which are of prime foraging importance to the species.

Some of the highest breeding densities in Britain occur on traditionally managed farmland estates which support a mixed system of farming and where game-rearing and fish management are practised. To support these farming and sporting interests, a mixture of landscape features such as small fields enclosed by deep hedgerows, wide field headlands, water meadows, rivers, streams and woodland are managed in a way which provides a mosaic of vegetation differing in composition and density. The mixed features within this overall habitat support substantial populations of small mammals as well as a diversity of species.

Unlike the permanent pastures and extensive grassland edges on traditional farmland, large cereal fields and closed-canopy coniferous forests support very low densities of small mammals, especially voles and shrews which require tussocky grass in which to feed and nest. When Wood Mice and Brown Rats *Rattus norvegicus* occur in fields of cereals or roots, the tall cover provided by these crops in summer severely restricts the Barn Owl's foraging. When foraging does occur, it is notably concentrated along tractor wheel tracks and in those areas where the standing crop has become flattened by wind or rain.

Barn Owls are therefore generally rare in those areas in which farming is predominantly of a single enterprise. In much of East Anglia tillage constitutes 75%-95% of crops and grass. In north Lancashire, Staffordshire, Cheshire, east Devon, west Dorset and Avon stocking densities reach levels of between 50-70 livestock units per 100 acres (40 ha) of agricultural land (Coppock 1976). In these situations the use of agricultural land has been maximised to such an extent that it can no longer provide habitat suitable for maintaining thriving small mammal populations.

The Supreme Importance of Grassland Edge

It can now be shown however, that it is possible for Barn Owls to attain densities similar to those of traditional farmland, even where vast monocultures of food crops or commercial woodland provide some of the most intensive and apparently inhospitable types of land management. In order for this to occur, particular features are required within this habitat. It is from the population anomalies which have been observed on two of the most intensively farmed areas in the Fenlands of Lincolnshire and the mosslands of Lancashire, that the primary foraging features for this species have been identified from the present *Survey*.

The one feature common to all habitats, whether they be traditional, intensively farmed or afforested, is the presence of unmanaged wet grassland margins (Figure 6). In the majority of these situations, boundary posts and hedgerow provide an important alternative means of 'perch and wait' hunting when aerial quartering becomes inefficient during periods of severe weather. In Lincolnshire and Lancashire, these hunting grounds are provided by the complex network of drainage dykes, drains and ditches, criss-crossing arable lands on which tussocky and luxuriant grass is continually fed by the nitrogen-rich drainage of adjacent fields. Not only are Short-tailed Voles, Common Shrews and Water Voles *Arvicola terrestris* abundant here but the restricted nature of these narrow grassland corridors provides the Barn Owl with a concentrated food source over a set beat from which familiarity produces high and efficient capture rates.

In northern Britain too, it has been found that coniferous woodland edge can provide a prime hunting ground for this species in a predominantly moorland and forest habitat (Taylor 1984). The boggy land on which many of these forests are planted and from which rank grassland rapidly develops following the removal of sheep, once again provides a high concentration of Short-tailed Vole and shrew both in the young plantations and later around the wet furrowed edges of the more mature forest.

Elsewhere in Britain, the Barn Owl is closely tied to those areas adjacent to the major rivers, wetlands and coastal marshes. So strong is this association that habitat analysis confirms that the bird's distribution throughout most of Britain closely mirrors the river networks and remaining wetland areas.

The Barn Owl's particular abundance on farmland dissected by river valleys may be a reflection of the less intensive nature of farming on the more waterlogged soils. However, the importance of wet unimproved or permanent grasslands for maintaining high populations of voles, has previously been identified for the Short-tailed Vole (Wendland 1984), Bank Vole and Water Vole (Corbet and Southern 1977) and for small rodents in particular (Honer 1963). Indeed this is considered to be the optimal grassland type for these species. Certainly, the moist and warm river valleys, like the artificial drainage channels, provide, over a prolonged growing season, the lush grasslands on which the voles depend. The traditional water meadow which, when flooded with warm waters in early Spring to promote an early bite of grass for sheep and cattle, has, for example, long been known as, and still remains, a favoured hunting habitat for the Barn Owl.

Of nearly 1,000 ringed Barn Owls which have subsequently been recovered in Britain, 76% were found within 20 km of their ringing site (Lack 1986), indicating the reluctance of young birds to move very far. For an inexperienced fledgling seeking independence, however, the need to move out of the natal territory along grasslands rich in prey, is of prime importance for survival. It is probably the linear aspects of the grasslands along rivers, streams, canals and drains which makes the Barn Owl's association with these habitat features so pronounced. It follows therefore, that dispersal along defined wet grassland routes, where prey is abundant, is likely to be the most effective means of eventually finding mates, and thereby maintaining local population levels. The importance of these findings is reflected in the 'Conservation Plan for the British Isles' in Part IV of this report.

The Size of Territories

Ticehurst (1935) considered that a pair of Barn Owls occupying prime habitat would require at least 51 ha of grassland over which to feed.

From the present *Survey* it is now possible to provide some indication of the area, or more importantly the length, of grassland edge available to those birds which today occupy prime habitats. This has been achieved by selecting and studying the most densely populated 10-km squares, first in traditional habitat and secondly in intensively farmed Fenland habitat, where both populations appear close to their saturation limits. Any

*2. Old farm buildings and derelict cottages provide the most important nest sites in the British Isles.
(D. Green)*

3. Tree cavities provide an alternative breeding site. In eastern regions of England they are used in preference to man-made structures.
(C. Fairweather)

4. Rock fissures in coastal cliffs and inland quarries are the third most important class of nest site. In the western regions of Scotland they often provide the only suitable nesting place.
(J. Orchel)

estimate of grassland requirement can nevertheless only be approximate since the Barn Owl is not strongly territorial and there is consequently often some overlap in hunting ranges between different pairs.

On the traditional estate which consisted of 4,800 ha, some 400 ha comprised woodland, though very little in blocks greater than 8 ha. Fields, of which most were arable, rarely exceeded 18 ha. Consequently the total length of hedgerow, woodland edge and accompanying wide headlands, which on this game-rearing estate were of good quality, amounted to 525 km in total length. The Barn Owl population here was 27 breeding pairs, thus providing a minimum of 17.6 km of grassland edge available to each pair. It should be noted also that the high density of Barn Owls was also partly attributable to the strict and efficient control of the ground predators, particularly the Fox *Vulpes vulpes*, Stoat *Mustela erminea* and Weasel *Mustela nivalis*, thus minimising competition for the vole.

In the Fenland situation, of the 9 pairs present within the most abundant 10-km square (10,000 ha), 200 km of drainage canals, ditches and roadside verges were present indicating that 22 km of grassland edge were available to each pair. (Interestingly, Shrubb (1984) has shown that in southern England the average hunting range of each of the 3 pairs studied by him included approximately 25 km of field boundary.) Since the water channels, and to some extent the roadside verges, were constructed to a uniform dimension throughout this habitat, the area of rough grassland available to each pair within these corridors could be calculated with some confidence at 44 ha.

The habitat needs of this species therefore appear to be critically dependent upon the length and quality of unmanaged grassland edge available within the hunting range which is probably of the order of 3 km². Assuming headland widths of 5 m, then 15-25 km of grassland edge appears necessary in order to support a breeding pair of Barn Owls on most farmland types in Britain.

The habitat diversity provided by rivers, streams, small fields, copses and wide headlands on many of our traditional estates, which generally have a prominent game-rearing interest, currently represent the optimum form of land management for this species. From the density data obtained from two of the most productive estates in Britain (both in terms of Barn Owl numbers and game bag totals) it is unlikely that Barn Owl levels on farmland could be expected to exceed densities of five or six pairs per 10 km².

The Choice of Roosting Sites
Trees appear to be an important day-time roost for Barn Owls even in areas where nest sites are more commonly to be found in buildings. Reports to the *Survey* indicate that the dense leafy foliage of many tree species, including ivy-covered stumps, is particularly attractive to young Barn Owls which have recently gained their independence. In regions of upland coniferous forest in Wales and Scotland, spruce and pine spp., provide a common roosting place, some of these sites being found deep within the forests.

NEST SITE SELECTION

The Barn Owl selects predominantly three distinct types of nest site in the British Isles: the interiors of buildings, large tree cavities and rock fissures. There is little suggestion that the selection of nest sites has changed greatly over the last two centuries. Pennant (1776) indicated that the species was similarly at home in trees as in buildings and 100 years later Yarrell and Newton (1871-1874) lists hollow trees second to church towers and farm buildings as the most usual site for nesting.

Blaker (1934) was the first to quantify the relative importance of these three sites in England and Wales, showing that 44% of the 915 nests found in 1932 were in hollow trees, 53% in buildings and 2.8% in cliff-like situations. Sharrock (1976) states that 39% of nest sites analysed by the BTO were in trees and Bunn *et al* (1982) provides a figure of 32% for this site, 65% in man-made structures and 3.2% in cliffs. Tables 3 – 7 provide a breakdown of nearly 2,700 nest sites recorded in this *Survey* and Figure 12 allows comparison with the data recorded in 1932.

Climatic Influences
It has in the past generally been believed that the Barn Owl is an opportunist in its choice of nesting site, selecting those sites most abundant in its particular area. The *Survey* has however established that the choice of nest site is not in fact based on simple opportunism but that, once again, climate appears to be a major factor in determining the type of breeding site selected.

Rainfall, like snowfall, varies considerably in different regions of the British Isles. However, unlike snowfall, which is more extensive in eastern regions, rainfall shows a reversal of this trend, being much heavier in the South and South-west, influenced by the prevailing moist south-westerly winds from the Atlantic. Throughout most of the western counties of Britain and Ireland, annual rainfall averages between 100 and 320 cm. Throughout much of eastern England however it rarely exceeds 65 cm. The marked regional differences are well illustrated in Map 7.

The Barn Owl is a bird poorly adapted for hunting in rain when its soft, little-oiled plumage rapidly becomes saturated, making hunting difficult. It has been previously indicated in this report that prolonged rainfall can seriously affect breeding success by reducing the amount of food which is provided by the male to the brooding female and dependent young. In addition, wet, and therefore ill-chosen, nest sites can rapidly lead to the death of young fledglings as a consequence of chilling and disease. Even after this most critical early period of nesting, heavy rainfall is known to be a particular hazard to newly emerging and therefore inexperienced young. These birds soon become waterlogged in their early attempts to become independent, often resulting in their inability to return to the security of the breeding site, and failure to survive.

For a species so susceptible to wet conditions, it would

NEST SITE SELECTION IN THE BRITISH ISLES

TABLE 3

Major Types of Nest Site

	ENGLAND		WALES		SCOTLAND		IRELAND		**BRITISH ISLES**	
	No of sites	% of known sites	No of sites	% of known sites	No of sites	% of known sites	No of sites	% of known sites	**No of sites**	**% of known sites**
Building	1115	64.68	118	90.08	229	81.21	96	82.05	**1558**	**69.12**
Tree	600	34.80	10	7.63	25	8.87	19	16.24	**654**	**29.02**
Cliff/Cave	9	0.52	3	2.29	28	9.93	2	1.71	**42**	**1.86**
Not known	342		28		68		7		**445**	
TOTAL	**2066**		**159**		**350**		**124**		**2699**	

TABLE 4

Type of Building

	ENGLAND		WALES		SCOTLAND		IRELAND		**BRITISH ISLES**	
	No of sites	% of known sites	No of sites	% of known sites	No of sites	% of known sites	No of sites	% of known sites	**No of sites**	**% of known sites**
Agricultural	845	75.78	91	77.12	137	59.83	10	10.42	**1083**	**69.51**
Domestic	107	9.60	18	15.25	71	31.00	22	22.92	**218**	**13.99**
Industrial	64	5.74	4	3.39	2	0.87	2	2.08	**72**	**4.62**
Castle	3	0.27			8	3.49	56	58.33	**67**	**4.30**
Church	39	3.50	4	3.39	3	1.31	4	4.17	**50**	**3.21**
Mill	17	1.52			4	1.75	2	2.08	**23**	**1.48**
Dovecote	16	1.43	1	0.85	1	0.44			**18**	**1.16**
Bridge	13	1.17			1	0.44			**14**	**0.90**
Oasthouse	7	0.63							**7**	**0.45**
Mine	3	0.27			2	0.87			**5**	**0.32**
Others	1	0.09							**1**	**0.06**
TOTAL	**1115**		**118**		**229**		**96**		**1558**	

TABLE 5   **Species of Tree**

	ENGLAND		WALES		SCOTLAND		IRELAND		**BRITISH ISLES**	
	No of sites	% of known sites	No of sites	% of known sites	No of sites	% of known sites	No of sites	% of known sites	**No of sites**	**% of known sites**
Elm *(Ulmus L.)*	142	34.30			2	15.38	4	26.67	**148**	**33.18**
Oak *(Quercus L.)*	141	34.06	3	75.00	3	23.08	4	26.67	**151**	**33.86**
Ash *(Fraxinus L.)*	66	15.94	1	25.00	4	30.77			**71**	**15.92**
Willow *(Salix L.)*	23	5.56							**23**	**5.16**
Beech *(Fagus L.)*	11	2.66			3	23.08	6	40.00	**20**	**4.48**
Poplar *(Populus L.)*	9	2.17							**9**	**2.02**
Walnut *(Juglans L.)*	7	1.69							**7**	**1.57**
Sycamore *(Acer L.)*	6	1.45					1	6.67	**7**	**1.57**
Pine *(Pinus L.)*	4	0.97							**4**	**0.90**
Chestnut *(Aesculus L.)*	4	0.97							**4**	**0.90**
Birch *(Betula L.)*	1	0.24			1	7.69			**2**	**0.45**
Total known	**414**	**100**	**4**	**100**	**13**	**100**	**15**	**100**	**446**	**100**
Not specified	186		6		12		4		**208**	
TOTAL	**600**		**10**		**25**		**19**		**654**	

TABLE 6   **Position Within Agricultural Building**

	BRITISH ISLES	
	No of sites	**% of known sites**
In or on hay or straw	**185**	**38.78**
Roof space or ceiling	**111**	**23.27**
In nest box supplied	**111**	**23.27**
On or in wall	**54**	**11.32**
In water tank	**16**	**3.35**
Total known	**477**	**100**
Not specified	**606**	
TOTAL	**1083**	

TABLE 7   **Position Within Domestic Building**

	BRITISH ISLES	
	No of sites	**% of known sites**
Roof space or ceiling	**63**	**55.75**
In nest box supplied	**1**	**0.88**
On or in wall	**6**	**5.31**
Inside chimney	**43**	**38.05**
Total known	**113**	**100**
Not specified	**105**	
TOTAL	**218**	

not be at all surprising to find that one of the most important requirements for breeding would be a site which remains relatively dry. In districts where rainfall is consistently heavy, the selection of more sheltered sites might be expected to be of prime importance.

This *Survey* has established that a marked variation in the choice of nest site does indeed occur and although the overall ratio of buildings to tree nest sites in England and Wales is 66:33, an overwhelming east-west deviation from this norm can be seen in those regions where opposing extremes of rainfall occur. In the southerly and westerly regions where rainfall is greatest, man-made structures are almost exclusively selected. For example, within the county of Devon in the extreme South-west, where rainfall is some of the highest in the British Isles, 95% of the breeding population nest in buildings. In the East, however, where rainfall is light and the winds drying, hollow tree sites predominate such that in Suffolk, the most easterly and driest county in Britain 70% of Barn Owls are tree nesters, twice the national average. The tight correlation between rainfall and regional nest site selection in the British Isles can be seen from comparison of Maps 6 and 7.

When the marked regional variation in nest site selection began to emerge, the research was taken a step further and the mean annual rainfall (1941-1971) was analysed for each of the 2,700 nest sites in the British Isles. The summarised results are presented in Figure 5 and once again it can readily be seen that nest site selection between buildings and trees can be positively related to the level of rainfall. In those regions where rainfall is above 70 cm, man-made structures take on increasing importance. Where rainfall exceeds 100 cm per year buildings constitute more than 90% of all nest sites. Conversely, below 70 cm tree sites show increasing significance and at the lowest rainfall of 55 cm encountered in the British Isles, over 70% are tree nesters compared with a nationwide average of just 29%. This analysis also shows that Barn Owls are rare in regions of high rainfall with only 5% of the breeding population being found where levels exceed 150 cm.

The fact that nest site selection does not simply reflect the greater abundance of trees in the East and buildings in the West can be illustrated by first studying two of the wettest counties, Devon and Sussex. These contain the highest numbers of mature hardwood trees, both in small woodland pockets and in hedgerows, and additionally have suffered less than most other southern counties from the loss of elms through Dutch Elm Disease. If opportunism was the sole factor determining nest site selection, it might reasonably be supposed that the percentage of trees used for nesting in these heavily timbered counties would at the very least exceed the average of 35% in England as a whole. Yet in Devon only 3% of tree sites are used and in Sussex, only 19%. Conversely, trees are less common in eastern England at only 0.6 per acre of farmland as compared to 1.5 nationally (Rackman 1986) but here tree sites are in fact favoured. Even in the most northerly latitudes of England the lack of suitable timber has previously been reported to limit tree-nesting by this species (Osbourne 1982; Bunn *et al*), but even here these natural sites can be shown to be more important in the east than in the wetter counties of the west. Proceeding north into Scotland,

suitable tree sites become uncommon but even if this were not so, it seems unlikely that these sites would be selected in high numbers in this country where rainfall is high throughout.

Only a small proportion of the county avifaunas published in the late 1800s gave sufficient detail about the major class of nest site used to allow comparison with the findings of the present survey. It is of interest to note, however, that those historic writers who were explicit indicated that, even then, trees were the predominant site in the eastern counties (Haines 1907; Steele-Elliott 1904; Lilford 1895; Christy 1890; Ticehurst 1932). Buildings, on the other hand, appeared to be the Barn Owl's exclusive choice in the western counties (Mitchell 1892; Mathew 1894; Wilson 1933) as they were in Sussex (Borrer 1891), and throughout much of Ireland (Ussher and Warren 1900) and Scotland (Gray and Anderson 1869; Gray 1871).

Whilst buildings are the most commonly used nest site in Scotland, rock fissures take on great importance especially around the coastal regions. This is particularly true in the West in Argyll and on the Inner Hebrides where cliffs and caves constitute about 50% of the total breeding sites. In these regions, the choice of nest site is more restricted than elsewhere, with suitable buildings and trees being far from common. Here, rock crevices and cavities in earthen cliffs and banks sometimes provide the only secure site for nesting and in contrast to the situation elsewhere, nest selection could confidently be described as opportunist in nature.

In recent decades there have been major alterations in habitat and farming methods, together with an increase in the Tawny Owl population, all factors which might be considered to have modified the Barn Owl's choice of nesting site. Despite these changes there appears to have been no evidence of regional differences in nest site selection over the last hundred years. This lends further support to the view that rainfall, a relatively stable long-term natural phenomenon, remains the major determinant of the class of nest site chosen in the different regions of the British Isles.

Successful fledging is therefore not only influenced by the availability of sufficient prey, the importance of which has previously been discussed, but also by the original choice of the nest site itself. Sites within spacious old cottages and farm buildings, as opposed to small tree cavities, discourage the premature departure of young which can have disastrous consequences during prolonged wet weather of the type more common in Ireland and the south-western regions of Britain. Filmed observations of Barn Owl nest sites confirm that having left the nest itself, the young often spend many days within the sheltered confines of the building exercising and practising the early development of hunting technique, before venturing forth. In the drier climates of the East, the need for sheltered sites is unlikely to be nearly so critical, and the relative lack of human disturbance associated with isolated hedgerow and parkland trees, perhaps makes them the preferred site.

In the USA the variation in rainfall from West to East is far more marked than it is in the British Isles and once again it has been reported by Bunn *et al* (1982) that the habit of nesting in trees is much more frequent in the drier West than in many of the heavier rainfall regions of

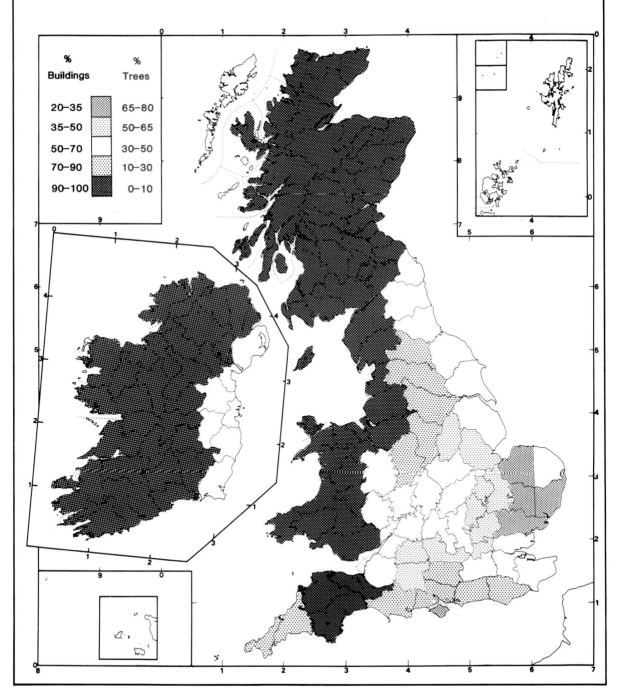

Map 6 *Nest site selection.*

This map illustrates the marked regional variation of the two major classes of nest site selected by Barn Owls in the British Isles. The relative percentages of man-made structures and trees are shown for each Vice-county (or district for parts of Scotland and Ireland).

% Buildings	% Trees
20–35	65–80
35–50	50–65
50–70	30–50
70–90	10–30
90–100	0–10

Rainfall

*Map 7 **Annual rainfall.***

Rainfall totals are based on the 1941–1970 average for Britain and 1931–1960 average for Ireland. The marked east-west variation in rainfall level can be seen.

Used in conjunction with Map 6 this rainfall map shows that in areas where rainfall is maximal (100–320 cm) over 90% of Barn Owls select more sheltered man-made structures for nesting. At the lower rainfall levels (50–60 cm), nest sites within trees are the more common site.

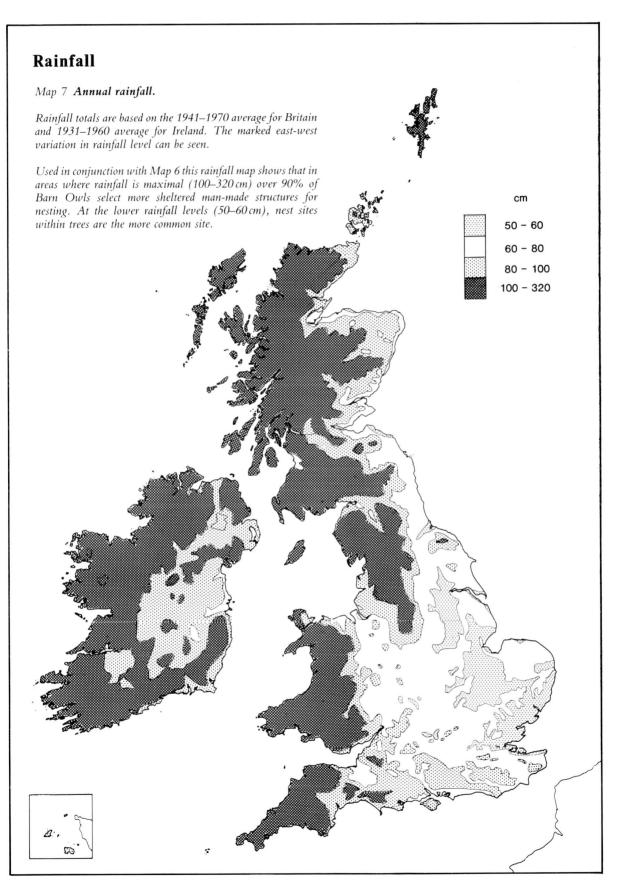

cm

50 – 60
60 – 80
80 – 100
100 – 320

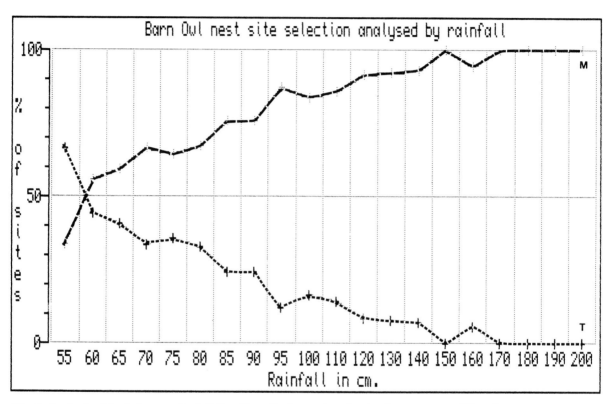

Fig. 5 *Analysis of the influence of rainfall on Barn Owl nest site selection between trees (T) and man-made structures (M) expressed as a percentage of all such sites at each rainfall level.*

the eastern states.

Perhaps in western Europe too, where very few Barn Owls are tree nesters, climate plays an important part. Certainly, this species is more commonly reported nesting in trees in parts of southern France and Spain where rainfall is far lighter than that found elsewhere in north-western Europe.

Imprinting on Nest Sites

In counties like Devonshire where nest sites are almost exclusively of one type, namely in buildings, the maintenance of this apparently successful trait is probably something which is either conditioned or learned. Perhaps the most obvious mechanism by which this occurs, is that birds remain imprinted for life on the type of site from which they fledged. As a result of the Barn Owl's particularly sedentary nature, with less than 25% of young birds dispersing further than 20 km from their birth place, it might indeed be expected that communities become established which are highly selective in their choice of nesting place. It can be seen that this appears to be true throughout most of the western and extreme southern counties as well as on the island of Anglesey, where 98% of the population nest in man-made structures, and on the Isle of Wight where 80% are tree-nesting birds.

In contrast to these single choice areas, Barn Owls in much of central England are less specific in their nest site selection and switching from building to tree, and vice versa, is not an infrequent occurrence at certain long observed sites. Assuming that imprinting governs the adults' nest selection then the switching of sites may merely indicate that a new mate has been taken, itself imprinted on a different site from the former partner, or that a new pair has become established.

Whatever the reason for the maintenance of these discrete building and tree-nesting communities, there is little doubt that the marked regional variation in nest site selection does occur and that this appears to be closely correlated with rainfall intensity in the British Isles. This now gives us the opportunity to target, at a county level, those sites most in need of protection, as well as providing a guide to the most effective placement of nestboxes in the future. This topic is more fully discussed in Part IV of this report.

The Choice of Tree Species

Whilst some Barn Owls will select trees for nesting in dense woodland, at the ends of forest rides for example, this species much prefers isolated trees in pastures and hedgerows. Trees more than 200 years old still remain a distinctive but nevertheless declining feature of both traditional farmland and old parkland in England.

From Table 4, it can be seen that the Oak *Quercus*, Elm *Ulmus* and Ash *Fraxinus* are the three most commonly occupied trees, undoubtedly because they are the most abundant deciduous species in the British Isles, and are notable for their cavity formation. Whilst oak is a more important species of woodland and parkland, the elm and ash remain the most common trees in hedgerows. However, any of these species can predominate locally although the oak is usually in the majority on less heavy soils.

It is generally the more ancient tree which provides the dry and spacious cavities which are favoured by the Barn Owl for nesting. Most nest sites (85%) are situated in the main trunk or in the case of pollards often the crown, whilst the remainder are in hollow branches (Glue in Bunn *et al* 1982). The long-lived nature of the oak and elm enables these trees to gain sufficient girth (20 ft recorded in one 300 year old elm) eventually to provide the cavernous rotted-out sites which are preferred. Not many farmland oaks however are more than 200 years old and it is often the antiquated pollards, usually between 200–600 years of age, in parkland, farmland and along roadsides, which provide cavities of sufficient size for nesting. Many parkland oaks which are occupied are of even greater age, one of the oldest being 1,000 years old. It is in one of these that Barn Owls continue to nest, having been described here since 1737 and possibly long before. Pollarded willows *Salix* spp. are the fourth most commonly used tree species. Although seldom of great age, the willow becomes important in Wiltshire, Somerset and parts of the Fenland.

The English Elm *Ulmus procera* has suffered greatly since Dutch Elm Disease, a fungal infection *Ceratocystis ulmi* spread by beetles *Scolytus* spp., took firm hold in southern Britain in the late 1960s. Whilst the effect of this disease has ravaged the English countryside and much concern has been voiced regarding the loss of nest sites for Barn Owls, the *Survey* has shown that the elm continues to remain, along with the oak, the most important tree nest site in the British Isles.

Dutch Elm Disease has spread rapidly since 1971, when less than 30% of the elms south of a line between Merseyside and the Wash were found to be dead or dying. By 1975 this had increased to 50% and by 1986 over 90% were severely diseased or had died. Once infection enters a tree, it can spread at a metre an hour, and whilst the period to death can be just a few days, the tree generally remains standing for many more years in the absence of being felled. Although in East Sussex sanitation felling is still successfully practised, the 1971 Dutch Elm Disease Local Felling Order was dropped in 1972, soon after its inception, and as a result few other counties have made any major attempts to remove diseased and dead farmland elms.

In spite of a study conducted in 1978 which suggested that Dutch Elm Disease may be an important factor contributing to the decline in Barn Owl numbers in southern Britain (Osbourne 1982), it would appear that the current loss of over eleven million farmland elms (Osbourne 1981) has not yet in fact led to any decline in the extent to which this tree is used by Barn Owls in Britain (currently 33% of total tree sites). Indeed, the proportion of elms to other tree sites used appears similar to that indicated by Blaker in 1932, and almost the same as during the period 1945 to 1978 when the elm was reported to represent 37% of all trees selected (Osbourne 1982). Not only is this true nationally, but even in the most severely diseased regions of the midland and central-southern counties which have lost over 90% of their elms, this percentage is still maintained (Appendix III). This strongly indicates that the decline of this nesting site is not yet a factor limiting the species' breeding requirements in the British Isles.

In the mid-1970s the elm undoubtedly provided more potential nest sites for this bird than at any time in its

Fig. 6 **Diagramatic representation of the major hunting habitats utilised by Barn Owls.**

These habitats have one particular feature in common. They are usually linear corridors, over 5 m wide, of essentially unmanaged, damp, tussocky grassland or marsh, bounded by posts or hedgerow. In these 'grassland edge' habitats, small mammal densities are generally higher than in less protected areas of open grassland. The boundary features additionally provide Barn Owls with perches for 'still hunting'. These are of particular importance during periods of prolonged snowcover, continuous rainfall or high winds when flight hunting becomes difficult and less efficient. Equally these linear grasslands are especially important in providing prey-rich dispersal corridors for young Barn Owls.

(a) **Riverside** *A prime habitat. Occurs locally throughout the British Isles.*

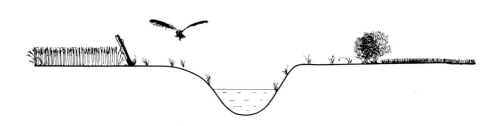

(b) **Ditchside** *Occurs commonly in the Fenlands of East Anglia, the Mosslands of south-west Lancashire and on the Somerset Levels.*

(c) **Banked Hedgerow** *A favoured hunting habitat in the south-west of England, parts of coastal Wales and Anglesey.*

(d) **Coastal Marsh and Water Meadow** *An important habitat around the coastal regions of eastern England and in the South adjacent to chalky rivers and streams.*

(e) **Young Commercial Plantation** *A prey-rich grassland habitat following the removal of sheep and the planting of young trees. Hunting is usually confined to the edges of adjacent mature woodland and along the drainage ditches between the young plantings.*

(f) **Traditional Estate/Parkland** *Mixed habitat features including 'woodland edge' combine to provide a diversity of prey species. Wide field headlands, commonly set aside for game, provide important foraging areas for Barn Owls.*

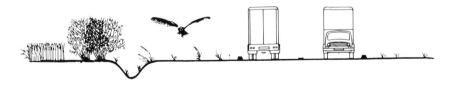

(g) **Roadside verge** *A major habitat especially attractive to young Barn Owls. Responsible for very high levels of mortality. Commonly used where grassland is lacking on adjacent farmland.*

The creation of new foraging habitat for Barn Owls on farmland should attempt to mimic these types of rough 'grassland edge' by expanding field headlands to a width of 5–10 m giving major priority to those areas along watercourses.

history. Hollow trunks were soon revealed by the spread of fungal disease and trees shed huge branches, encouraging the more rapid advancement of decay and yielding a greater surplus of cavities then ever before. The peak period of nest site suitability in elms would have occurred in central-southern England between 1975 and 1978 when the majority of trees were in an advanced stage of disease but before the large proportion had fallen or been felled. Even today, in a county such as Wiltshire which has lost virtually all of its 1.1 million elms, 56% of Barn Owls are tree nesters and of these 23% still find enough elms in which to nest successfully.

To date this disease has been far less aggressive both in Cornwall, where *Ulmus procera* is replaced by the Cornish Elm *Ulmus angustifolia*, and in East Sussex partly as a result of sanitation felling where currently 53,000 elms remain (Richards pers. comm). In Suffolk and parts of east Essex too, only 50-70% of elms were affected in 1983 compared with 90% elsewhere in southern Britain; perhaps this reflects the counties' isolation from the heavily infected areas inland or the preponderance of a different sub-species *Ulmus carpinifolia* and other hybrids.

Whilst parts of these counties are still comparatively free of Dutch Elm Disease, it nevertheless seems unlikely that Suffolk will escape the full ravages of tree loss which have occurred elsewhere. This could have more serious consequences for the Barn Owl in a county boasting the highest percentage of tree nesters in the British Isles. Analysis shows however, that of about 150 Barn Owl pairs present in Suffolk, only 18% are elm tree nesters. It would seem probable that the eventual loss of the elm (and at the start of this *Survey* around 540,000 remained in Suffolk), is unlikely to limit the population even here from maintaining its current numbers. Over 150,000 mature but partially decaying oak and ash trees exist in the county, sufficient to provide alternate sites in the forseeable future.

In spite of the subsequent grubbing out of a great many hedges with their associated trees between 1954-1980 and the devastation of Dutch Elm Disease, there appears to have been little change in the proportion of tree sites selected by the Barn Owl over the last fifty years. Indeed, neither has there been any obvious indication of a redistribution of tree species which have been used for nesting since 1932 when there had been comparatively little destruction from either disease or man.

The Choice of Man-made Structures

The relative proportions of the different classes of man-made sites which are most commonly used by the Barn Owl for nesting are shown in Table 4, and their preferences within these structures is further sub-divided in Tables 6 and 7.

In the British Isles, agricultural buildings represent 70% of this major class of site, followed by domestic dwellings (14%), industrial or commercial buildings, in which water towers were included (4.6%), 'castles' (4.3%) and churches (3.2%). Other sites individually represented less than 1.5% of the remaining breeding places.

The *Survey* found that the majority of nests in farm buildings were in places subject to some form of agricultural use as opposed to entirely derelict structures. However, only rarely were the nest sites themselves exposed to daily human activity. Hay and pigeon lofts, holes in walls, bale stacks and nest-boxes usually provided the necessary seclusion. In contrast, the nest sites found within the majority of domestic and industrial buildings were in derelict structures. Domestic buildings took on additional importance in northern England and Scotland where disused cottages were more commonplace, often vacated as a result of changes in agricultural practice or afforestation.

Churches, some of which were disused, still accounted for 3.2% of man-made structures, probably much the same percentage as in Blaker's day when domestic dwellings and churches in a class together accounted for 13% of total nest sites. This suggests that although churches were once a common site, their accessibility became limited as early as 1932 as a result of the towers being wired off from Jackdaws and pigeons by the Ecclesiastical Commissioners.

Nesting on or within loose hay and straw, or more usually bales, is very common, with 39% of all notified nests in agricultural buildings being found in this situation. In Blaker's day too, breeding in this site was common with the ricks and hay-filled lofts providing the nesting places. Whilst these particular sites provide a high degree of security at the beginning of the year, they become extremely vulnerable as bales are progressively removed during the Spring.

In domestic buildings, the space on the ceiling boards between the joists of upper floors and attics provides the most common nesting place and blocked chimneys are the alternative site. Nests on or within stone walls account for many of the remaining breeding locations within buildings. Included in this category are those breeding places in disused cavities and heating ducts in old Victorian walled gardens for example.

Nestboxes and barrels appear to provide an important proportion of known nest locations within agricultural buildings (23%). This apparently encouraging total should however be interpreted with caution. At least half of the artificial sites which have been erected over the last thirty years have been positioned at existing breeding places, and have therefore not created additional sites. Often, this has been undertaken to allow research activities to be carried out more easily. Nevertheless, the fact that these birds are using the boxes in preference to the traditional crevice or ledge within a building bears some testimony to their secure nature. Nationally, nestboxes assume a prime importance as a substitute for insecure nesting sites, particularly those on or within hay or straw bales.

Of those breeding sites of secondary importance, watermills and windmills comprised this sub-class. Freestanding dovecotes were next in order of importance and old railway bridges constituted the majority of bridge sites, although in three instances modern concrete motorway type bridges spanning busy highways were used. Oasthouses were more commonly found in southeastern England and nesting below ground in mine shafts occurred on five occasions.

Disused, often ruined 'castles', although uncommon in the British Isles, were of primary importance in the Republic of Ireland. Agricultural sites were however conspicuously absent with only 10% of the breeding population occupying farm buildings. This perhaps reflects a greater degree of disturbance and persecution and possibly the impact of rodenticide poisoning on birds in more intimate contact with man.

Multiple-Breeding at a Single Site

'Owleries' were described in Britain in the 1800s in which at least thirty to forty Barn Owls were found occupying a collection of cottages with interconnecting roof spaces. (Durban and Mathew 1895). Presumably this may have represented at least six families. Other instances refer to over a dozen adult owls with young at a single breeding site in the roof of a country house (Mathew 1894). Communal nesting has also been described more recently from France and America (Baudvin 1974, Marti in Bunn *et al* 1982).

During the present *Survey* a single pair of Barn Owls was reported to have taken up residence for the first time in the roof of a large country farmhouse in the late 1970s. In 1983, two pairs were reported to have bred and in 1984, numbers had increased to three pairs. In 1985 one of the pairs changed their allegiance to a tree alongside the house. Although the roof design was such that the birds could be inspected from an attic hatchway, breeding success was unknown. However, the activity patterns of the adults during the breeding season in 1984 confirmed that all three pairs were feeding young and that whilst ranges overlapped over meadow land and an adjacent pig farm, it was uncommon for two pairs simultaneously to select the same area for hunting.

In 1985, two nest sites, less than 10 m apart, were observed by the author within a derelict farmstead in a remote area of south-west Scotland. One site contained four full grown young and the other a single four week old owlet. This suggested two adult females tended by a single male. Bigamous mating was confirmed at the same site in 1987 when two very young broods accompanied by two female birds were found in different locations within these old buildings (Orchel pers. comm.).

Instances of other birds of prey occupying the same site were not uncommon. Usually this referred to Kestrels *Falco tinnunculus* and Little Owls *Athene noctua* at both barn and tree sites. In one instance all three species successfully fledged from the same bale stack. There were however only two reports of Tawny Owls nesting alongside Barn Owls. The first was at a traditional Barn Owl site from which the Tawny Owls were evicted causing them to desert their young. At the other site Barn Owls failed at the egg stage for reasons which were unknown.

Fidelity to Breeding Sites

Barn Owls maintain a very strong and intimate association with their chosen breeding sites, many of which are of great antiquity. Old diaries provided by some farmers to the *Survey* confirm continuous occupation of some sites for well over a hundred years and indications from other sources suggest some very old tree sites have been used for much longer periods of time. Traditional nest sites such as these are only vacated permanently when the surrounding habitat will not supply sufficient food or when the nesting place itself has been modified or destroyed.

Whilst many Barn Owl pairs will occupy their breeding quarters throughout the year, the *Survey* has also shown that about half will vacate their sites following the breeding season, only taking up residence again during February or March the following year. Whilst this was commonly found to be the case with birds occupying marginal habitats above 100 m, it also occurred frequently on lowland farms, especially those which lacked hay or straw filled barns. Conversely, other respondents reported that the only time Barn Owls were observed on their farms was during the winter period. Almost always the birds were associated with hay barn sites, providing some confirmation of the importance of this micro-habitat in winter and the availability of commensal rodents.

BREEDING PERFORMANCE

The overall breeding success of a population can be measured in terms of the numbers of pairs attaining breeding condition and attempting to lay eggs, the clutch size, hatching success and finally the numbers of young birds which eventually fledge from the nest site.

Comparison of Productivity over the last Fifty Years

In 1932, Blaker conducted a study of 214 nests in England and Wales which were followed through the breeding season from the completion of clutches to eventual fledging. From an analysis of these nests he found an average clutch size of 3.8 from which 2.8 young were successfully reared.

These figures were obtained during a single year of study and must of course be viewed with some caution when comparing them with breeding success today. Historically, however, Blaker's study provides the only baseline on which present trends can be assessed, and it is perhaps reassuring that the year both preceding his study, and over which the study was conducted, had mild winters and according to Snow (1968) vole numbers were considered good. Tentatively then, it would appear that these figures provide some indication of the average breeding success in England and Wales fifty years ago.

Glue (in Bunn *et al* 1982) has analysed the outcome of 155 Barn Owl clutches recorded in the British Isles over more recent years (predominantly between 1960-1980) Translating these figures in a similar way to those of Blaker (ie from all nests successful or otherwise), it can be shown that for completed clutches, 4.7 eggs were produced and 2.2 young fledged.

The apparently lower fledging success indicated by these more recent data may imply an increased level of human disturbance during the nesting period or a shortage of food resulting in nest desertion by the brooding female and the direct starvation of nestlings. In spite of the more intensive use of farm buildings today, it seems unlikely that human disturbance differs markedly from that in 1932 when, as Blaker noted, egg and skin collecting contributed in a significant way to breeding failure. (Possibly the reason for the particularly low average clutch size observed). It would seem more probable, therefore, that the combination of worsening annual snowfall, changing agricultural practices, and the resultant decline in prey, are the most likely factors responsible for the apparent reduction in fledging success

BREEDING PERFORMANCE OF BARN OWLS
IN THE BRITISH ISLES 1982–1986

TABLE 8

**Average clutch size and fledging rate
in the British Isles**

Year	Clutch size	n	Number fledged	n
1982	4.88	(9)	2.77	(31)
1983	4.43	(14)	3.13	(67)
1984	5.30	(20)	3.36	(78)
1985	5.20	(41)	2.94	(62)
1986	4.51	(41)	2.80	(52)
All:	4.86		3.00	

TABLE 10

**Frequency of clutch size and fledging rate
in the British Isles**

Clutch size	No nests	%	Number fledged	No broods	%
1	1	0.80	1	33	11.38
2	4	3.20	2	75	25.86
3	18	14.40	3	81	27.93
4	25	20.00	4	58	20.00
5	37	29.60	5	32	11.03
6	24	19.20	6	9	3.10
7	11	8.80	7	2	0.69
8	4	3.20	8	0	0.00
9	1	0.80	9	0	0.00
n = 125			n = 290		

'Fledged' refers to large young leaving, or preparing to
leave the nest.

TABLE 9

**Comparison of clutch size and fledging rates
in England & Wales and in Scotland**

	Clutch size	n	Number fledged	n
England & Wales	5.24	(37)	3.35	(155)
Scotland	4.72	(88)	2.84	(135)

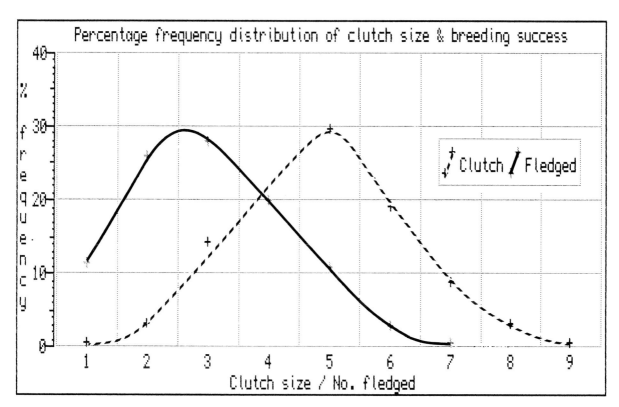

Fig. 7 *Broken line – Clutch size expressed as a percentage of 125 successful clutches recorded for the* **Survey.**
Solid line – Number of Barn Owls fledged expressed as a percentage of 290 broods recorded for the **Survey.**

TABLE 11 **Percentage fledging success rate in some European countries in relation to Latitude**
(Partly after Mikkola, 1983)

	Clutch size	(n)	Number fledged	(n)	Success rate %	Latitude
Sweden	4.63	(33)	2.15	(36)	46	56.0
Scotland	4.72	(88)	2.84	(135)	60	55.0
England & Wales	5.24	(37)	3.35	(155)	64	53.0
East Germany	5.77	(126)	3.84	(141)	67	52.5
Holland	4.03	(705)	3.20	(507)	79	52.0
West Germany	5.51	(354)	4.38	(354)	79	52.0
France★	6.22	(269)	4.54	(512)	73	47.0
Switzerland	5.33	(63)	4.50	(182)	84	47.0
EUROPE	5.18		3.60		69	

★ Includes many second clutches known for their large size

'Fledged' refers to large young leaving, or preparing to leave the nest

Latitude given refers to study area or site of major Barn Owl population density within the country since 1932.

Whilst the present *Survey* did not actively encourage the submission of information about the contents of nests, breeding records were nevertheless provided for 3% of the 2699 nest sites notified in the British Isles between 1982-1986. The sites from which breeding information was obtained were from well-distributed locations and, in geographical terms, were closely representative of the Barn Owl's relative abundance nationwide. As a result, the major proportion were from the southern regions of Scotland and from the higher density areas of England and Wales where populations were within the range of 6-12 pairs per 100 km². In terms of habitat, 87% of the sites in England and Wales could be reliably described as lowland farms less than 125 m above sea level, whilst in Scotland 85% were below 150 m.

Productivity in Britain between 1982 and 1986

Tables 8, 9, and 10 and Figure 7 show a breakdown of nesting success. These data have been presented in terms of the numbers of fledged birds arising out of nests where at least one young was successfully reared. Unlike the previous method used to calculate productivity, (which allowed comparisons to be drawn between 1932 and more recent years), nests which completely failed following the laying of a full clutch, were no longer included when determining mean clutch size and fledging success totals.

The lower overall productivity observed during 1982 and 1986 is reflected both in terms of reduced clutch sizes and fledging success rates (Table 8). This coincided with the two years during the *Survey* when snowcover was maximal and the population index was at its lowest level (Figure 3). Whilst clutch sizes were somewhat lower during these years, there was a higher incidence (especially in eastern England) of pairs not attempting to breed and of clutches which had failed completely.

In conclusion, it would appear that following winters where snowcover annually exceeds 20 days, breeding becomes less productive. This is the result of the increased failure of pairs to begin egg-laying, slightly lower clutch sizes in those which do, and finally a decrease in the brood size and overall fledging success.

Out of a total of 290 nests from which breeding data were gathered, fifteen instances of successful double-brooding were recorded. Two additional cases of triple-brooding were also reported in 1984 in Montgomery-shire and north Devonshire. It was interesting to note that between 1982-1986, the incidence of double-brooding was greatest in 1984 (the winter demonstrating a low level of snowcover), with seven cases reported. In 1985 a further five double-brooding events were notified. In contrast only two cases occurred in 1982 and none in either 1983 or 1986. In regional terms, out of a total of seventeen multiple-brooding events, fourteen were recorded from western counties of Britain in Devon, Somerset, Anglesey, Wigtown and Kirkcudbright. Once again, double-brooding appeared significantly more common during those years when winter climate, notably the duration of snowcover, was least severe.

The combined values for all four years throughout the British Isles result in an average clutch size of 4.86 and a fledging success of 3.00.

Comparative Productivity in England and Wales and in Scotland

When the overall breeding performance figures are subdivided between England/Wales and Scotland, there is a trend towards a lower clutch size and fledging success rate in Scotland (Table 9). There can, nevertheless, be much local variation in breeding performance within regions. It has for example been reported by two workers that lowland farms in Scotland maintain a lower but nevertheless more stable annual productivity, ranging between 2.2 and 2.9 young, whilst those in higher sheepwalk and forestry habitats nearby often fail to breed in some years and when they do show a less consistent productivity of between 1.1 and 5.3 young. (Taylor 1984; Orchel 1986). Undoubtedly, this indicates once again that in those years of climatic extreme (prolonged snowcover, continuous rainfall or drought), breeding becomes markedly less successful as altitude increases.

Long-term observations in Hertfordshire and sur-rounding counties, (where Barn Owl numbers are at critical levels of 0-2 pairs per 100 km²), whilst demonstrating insignificant variations in clutch size from the national average, show a markedly lowered fledging success. This rarely exceeds two fledged young per nest and has averaged only 1.9 in recent years at the few remaining sites in this part of England (Shawyer unpublished observations).

These local findings serve to illustrate the care which must be taken in arriving at and interpreting an average breeding performance figure for the country as a whole, for not only must a study of this nature cover at least one complete snow/vole cycle but the regions from which the nest data are selected must be representative of the species' overall abundance.

Comparative Breeding Performance in Europe

From Tables 8 and 11 it can be seen that the average clutch size in the British Isles of 4.86 compares favourably with the 4.95 found in Western Europe as a whole. The fledging success figure of 3.00 is however lower than the European average of 3.60. Whilst there is perhaps some slight indication of a reduced clutch size with increasing latitude throughout the countries of Europe, brood size shows a more obvious decreasing trend towards the north. The egg to fledging success rate demonstrates an even more significant loss in productivity from 84% in southern Europe (latitude 47°), to just 60% in Scotland (55°) and 46% in Sweden (56°).

It is interesting to note that close to the Equator in Peninsular Malaysia the mean clutch size for *T. a. javanica* has been recorded at 6.6. This is higher than that reported elsewhere in either temperate or tropical climates. The average brood size at fledging (second broods included) was 3.7. When first broods only were considered this figure rose to 4.5. In response to a stable climate and the exceptionally prey-rich habitat created by the oil palm, most pairs consistently produced two and some times three broods. This suggests an average annual productivity of at least 7.4 fledged young per pair (Lenton 1984).

It would appear therefore that a greater incidence of egg failure and/or brood depletion is the most significant cause of the lowered success rates at higher latitudes.

5. The remains of an old cottage chimney provide one of the last opportunities for nesting in an area of commercial forestry in south-west Scotland.
(J. Orchel)

45

6. *A family of four owlets about six weeks old showing their growth differences, the result of staggered hatching.* (D. Callan)

7. *The signs of a well-used Barn Owl roost with the floor strewn with pellets, 'whitewash' and moulted feathers.* (J. Orchel)

January temperatures are below 3.5 °C, snowcover is consequently more prolonged, and seasonal extremes of climate becomes more pronounced in these regions.

THE DECLINE OF THE BARN OWL OVER THE LAST FIFTY YEARS

PRIMARY CAUSES

The Effect of Climate

The influence of climate has, in the past, been largely neglected when attempting to understand the primary factors responsible for the decline of a number of bird species in Britain. For those birds at the limit of their range, even small changes in winter severity have the potential severely to reduce population levels. Should these climatic changes be part of a sustained worsening pattern, then numbers will generally show a long-term downward trend and, in situations of an already fragile population, they can lead to extinction. Steep population declines, especially those involving resident passerine and game bird species have, with the aid of ornithological statistics, been historically correlated with the arrival or intensification of particular types of detrimental agricultural practice and habitat loss. The findings which have emerged from this Barn Owl study suggest however that greater priority should be given to both the short and long-term consequences of climatic extremes, such as snowfall, drought and excess rainfall, prior to assessing the relevance of other less natural factors which may be contributing to the species' decline.

The effect of climate on the population level of the Barn Owl in the British Isles has been discussed in Part II of this report in terms of the periods of short-term cyclical decline which are a noticeable feature of this species' population dynamics. Climatic extremes, in particular prolonged periods of snowcover, were shown to be the most important factor influencing the population level of the Barn Owl through a lowering of its breeding potential as a result of a reduction in winter prey availability at the most critical period just prior to the nesting season. The sensitivity of this species to more than 20 days of lying snow in any one winter appears decisive for triggering an overall population crash, measured in terms of productivity in the following breeding season.

During prolonged periods of relatively stable climate, population settles at a level dependent upon the food supply and nest site availability within the selected habitat (assuming human pressures are not operative against the species). In the forty years between 1900-1939, the winter climate throughout the British Isles remained remarkably mild. The mean annual frequency of lying snow over this period was just 12 days and in only one of these forty winters did snow cover exceed 20 days (29 days in 1917). The Barn Owl population throughout this mild climatic period maintained itself at a substantially higher level than that observed today. From 1940, the winter climate changed so profoundly that the mean number of days of lying snow almost doubled over the period 1940-1986 and the critical 20 day snow lying threshold was reached and exceeded in

twenty-two of these forty-seven winters. Indeed, during nine of these seasons the frequency of lying snow exceeded 30 days and in the most severe winters of 1947, 1963 and 1979, a nationwide mean of over 40 days occurred. In summary, only 2.5% of the winters between 1900-1939 demonstrated more than 20 days with snow lying, whilst from 1940-1986, this figure increased substantially to 47%. This is illustrated dramatically in Figure 8, which shows, since 1900, the increasing frequency of winters when snow cover reached or exceeded 20 days, and in Figure 9 which shows the fifteen year moving average.

The marked deterioration in the winter climate had therefore become firmly established throughout the British Isles by the late 1940s, whereupon the Barn Owl population readjusted and later stabilised to a new and lowered baseline level of abundance as a result of a reduced level of breeding success. This would have been caused by a lowered prey availability itself a direct consequence of the increased and sustained winter severity.

Although it is difficult to determine precisely the beginnings of the long-term decline of Barn Owl numbers in this century, the majority of literature indications are that it began, or accelerated rapidly, during the late 1940s. This we now know was consistent with the start of a sudden and sustained worsening of the winter climate. The ringing records (Figure 3) empirically confirm the rapidly declining population trend which was occurring at that time (although this decrease may have been further compounded by some re-emergence of persecution after the Second World War).

Comparison of the present survey data with that from the 1932 census provides a measure of the extent of population decline which has taken place in England and Wales over the last fifty years. The most significant losses have occurred in those areas where snowcover is most prolonged and the evidence which follows confirms that the Barn Owl's long-term decline is predominantly the result of the continuing deterioration of the winter climate. These conclusions have been derived from an analysis of the extent of the changes in abundance which have occurred throughout the British Isles at both local and regional level.

Local Evidence

In 1932, the Barn Owl was shown to be equally abundant on land up to 400 m above sea level. Indeed, some of the highest densities at that time were identified in the northern lakeland districts of Cumbria at altitudes of between 200-400 m, the species being absent or rare in England and Wales only from the higher regions of the Pennines and Cambrian Mountains. It is significant also that it was here on the higher ground of Cumbria that an abnormal population increase was being observed at the time of the census in 1932, whilst in central and southern Scotland recovery had been observed somewhat earlier. Undoubtedly the Barn Owl's specific recolonisation of these otherwise colder northerly regions had been stimulated by the mild period of snow-free winters which had its beginnings in the British Isles some thirty years earlier and lasted until 1939.

Today, after almost fifty years of increased and sustained winter severity, the local status of the Barn

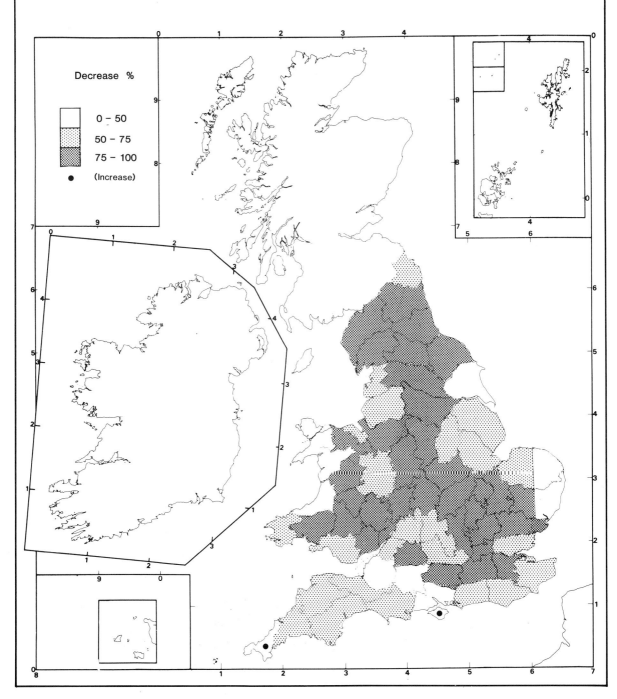

Map 8 **The extent of Vice-county population decline 1932–1985.**

Used in conjunction with Maps 9 and 10 it can be seen that the most pronounced Barn Owl losses have taken place in those regions where snowcover now exceeds 15 days per annum and mean January temperatures are below 3.5° C.

Decrease %

- 0 – 50
- 50 – 75
- 75 – 100
- (Increase)

Days Snow Lying

Map 9 **The average number of days with snow lying per year (1941–1970).**

Maps 9 and 10 demonstrate the marked regional variation in the mean number of days of annual snowcover and January mean temperatures in the British Isles (Met. Office 1975).

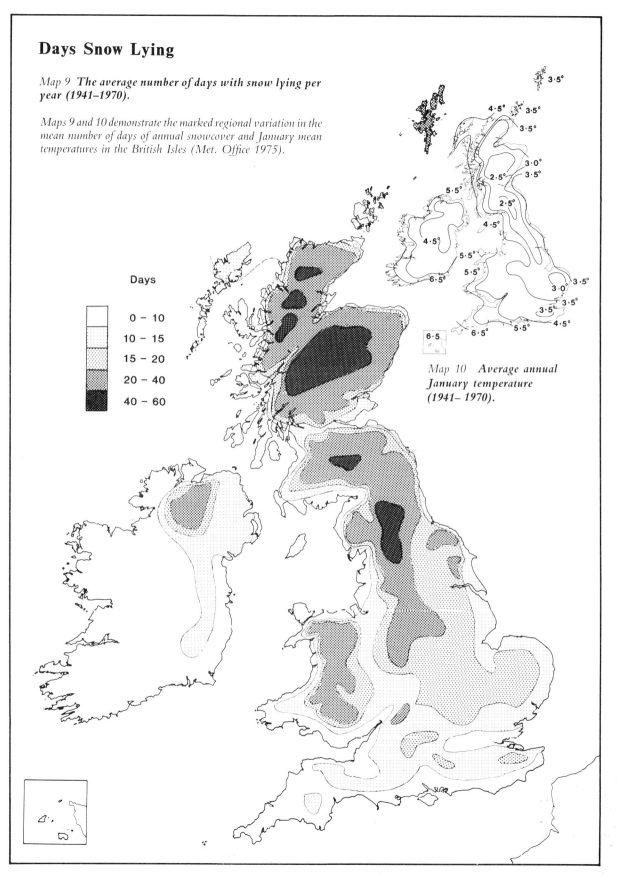

Days

	0 – 10
	10 – 15
	15 – 20
	20 – 40
	40 – 60

Map 10 **Average annual January temperature (1941– 1970).**

Owl has changed dramatically from its relatively high abundance in the 1930s. It is now uncommon or entirely absent from the majority of areas where the altitude exceeds 100 m. Indeed, analyses of data revealed that today only 18% of breeding sites are to be found above 100 m and as few as 7% exceed 150 m (Figure 4), with almost all of these occurring in the warmer extreme south-westerly regions of England and Scotland.

A comparison of the present Barn Owl population and land relief (Maps 5, 8 and 11) indicate that the major decline of this species has occurred, not only from true

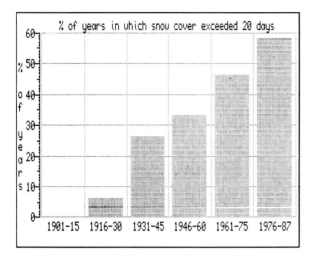

Fig. 8 **Percentage of years in each period in which average snowcover in the British Isles exceeded 20 days.**

upland regions above 300 m which include much of the north-east and central Scotland, Cumbria, West Yorkshire and all but the coastal districts of Wales; but also in the much lower-lying downlands of the southern counties. This includes the hills of the Cotswolds and Chilterns, the Northamptonshire uplands, extending into much of Leicestershire, the north Lincolnshire Wolds and south Staffordshire plateau, all areas where the land exceed 100 m.

Altitude dictates the number of days over which snow lies; for not only is snowfall heavier on higher ground but temperature falls with increasing altitude at a rate of about 1 °C for every 150 m. Snowcover itself therefore increases with elevation between 9-24 days per 150 m rise. The lower rate is applicable to the South Devonshire moors and the higher rate to the Central Highlands of Scotland (Met. Office 1975).

In terms of snow duration, land in the British Isles which rises 100 m or more above sea level (with the exception of the warmer extreme South-west) has since 1939 annually averaged 15-20 days of lying snow. Between 1900-1939 however, this higher ground averaged only 5-10 days. The decline of this species from the higher ground, since 1932, appears therefore to have been the result of the major increase in snowcover.

Topography therefore limits the Barn Owl population in the British Isles, and now places almost entire counties, including those of central-southern England, at the species' limits of suitability. This is by virtue of the fact that these counties possess substantial areas of land above 100 m which currently receive as much as 15-20 days mean annual snowcover. In those areas where snowcover annually exceeds 20 days, the Barn Owl is

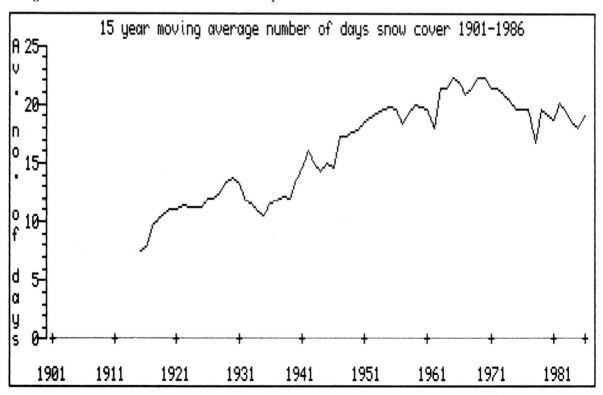

*Fig. 9. **Average number of days' snowcover in the British Isles expressed as a 15-year moving average.***

Altitude

Map 11 Altitude.

The 10 km squares shown in red indicate areas of land where over 30% of the square exceeds 100 m above sea level. They also correspond to the major centres of localised Barn Owl decline. These areas have, like those throughout eastern Britain, become marginal for this species as a consequence of an increased level of annual snowcover which has been most pronounced at these higher altitudes, averaging 15 days or more annually.

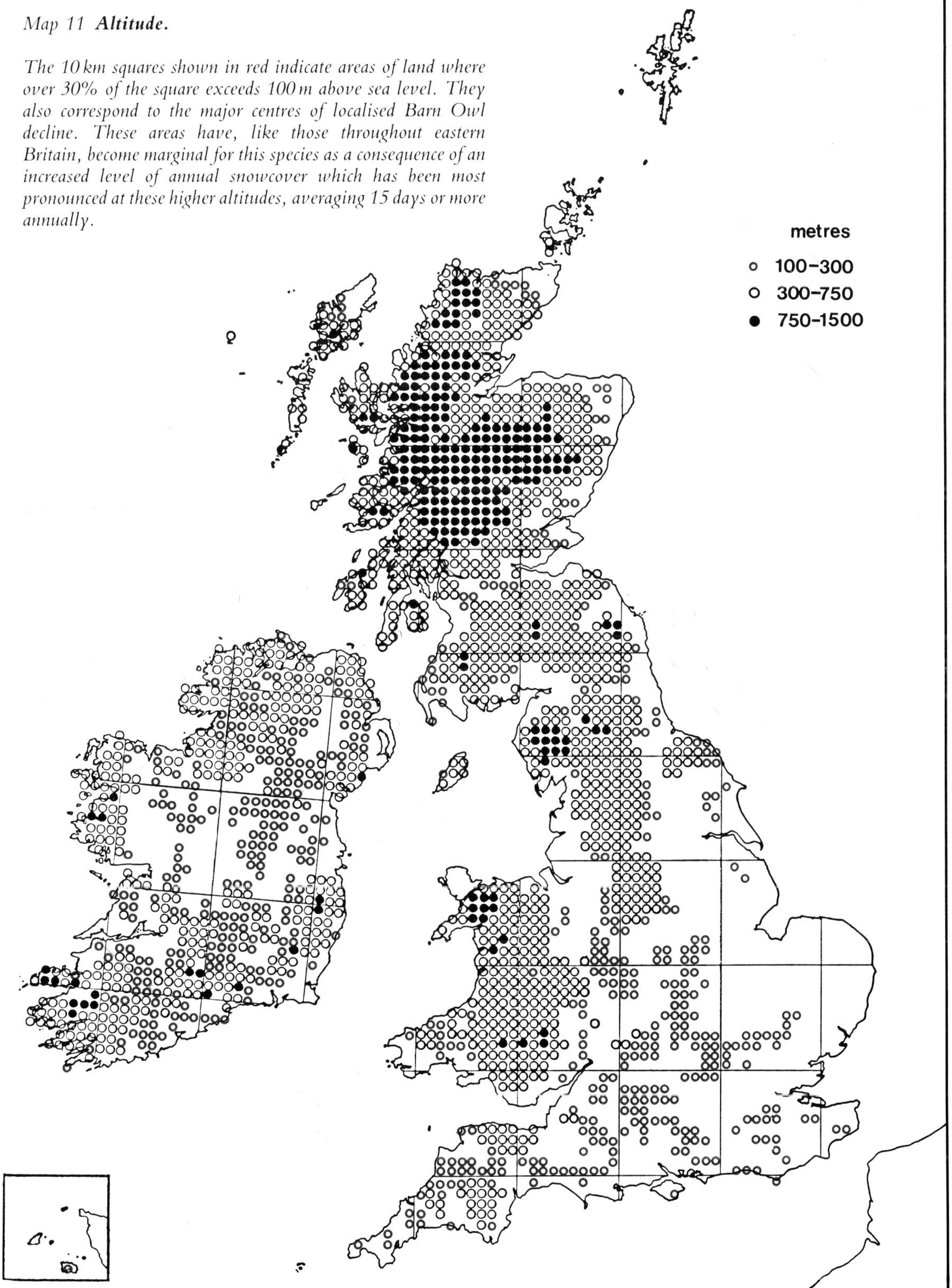

metres

○ 100–300
○ 300–750
● 750–1500

now a rare breeding bird.

Regional Evidence

Whilst an increased incidence of snow is confined on a localised basis to the higher ground throughout the British Isles, our winter climate also shows substantial regional variation. In the warm relatively snow-free winters of the South and South-west, January temperatures annually average 5-7 °C and the seasonal mean snowcover is just 5-10 days. In contrast, throughout the East and North, average winter temperatures are as low as 2.5-3.5 °C and seasonal snowcover averages 15-20 days (Maps 9 and 10).

A substantial decline in Barn Owl numbers has, as we have previously seen, taken place in those districts which exceed 100 m above sea level. A more widespread and major regional decline has also occurred throughout the low-lying inland regions of Essex, Suffolk, Norfolk, Leicestershire and west Lincolnshire which because of their eastern situation are both the snowiest and coldest in lowland Britain. The maps showing annual snowcover and January isotherms clearly demonstrate these regional climatic differences with frequencies of 15 or more days snow lying, and temperatures below 3.5 °C reflecting those regions of major Barn Owl decline (Map 8).

The increased frequency of lying snow since 1940 is therefore entirely consistent with the slow progressive decline which has occurred predominantly on the higher ground and throughout the lowlands of eastern England. With the exception of the warmer south-west counties, those regions above 100 m, and elsewhere in the British Isles where the snow duration approaches 15 days or more, must now be considered unsuitable and therefore very marginal for this species. Such areas are likely to be occupied temporarily only in the event of local population increase on adjacent low-lying lands following a spell of mild winters.

Effects of a Reduced Food Supply

In Winter

The Barn Owl is primarily a specialist predator of small field mammals with the Short-tailed Vole and Common Shrew providing the major food source on the mainland of England, Wales and Scotland. In spite of the Barn Owl's long-standing reputation as an efficient predator of commensal rodents, the Brown Rat and House Mouse *Mus musculus* today constitute only 12% by weight of the annual diet in the British Isles, although in Ireland and eastern England they provide 39% and 31% respectively (Glue 1974). However, these two commensals can, together with other less typical prey species such as small birds and insects, take on much greater overall significance by providing the major proportion of the diet during periods of winter hardship or when field prey is otherwise scarce. Indeed it would seem improbable that breeding condition could be maintained under such conditions without these alternative sources of prey.

Unlike the more stable situation which can occur in tropical climates, small mammal numbers in the British Isles fluctuate seasonally with the changing climate. As we have seen, when this winter prey becomes scarce, on snowcovered open farmland for example, the Barn Owl's future breeding productivity and long-term survival can be seriously reduced in the absence of an alternate or more readily derived food source.

An effective buffer against this seasonal reduction in field prey during severe winters was once provided by the corn-rick, a feature of the stackyard and barn of almost every farmstead throughout the nineteenth and earlier part of the twentieth century. Commonly, these stackyards consisted of between two and six individual ricks of wheat, oats or barley or occasionally beans, built in August and threshed at any time from September through to the following July.

A detailed study in the early 1940s by the Agricultural Research Council found that the corn-rick was a habitat of major importance for rats and mice, constituting their main winter breeding areas. The study, which was devised to assess the rodent numbers contained within these ricks, concluded that maximum densities were attained at the height of the winter season in February through to May, as a result of continuous breeding within this warm and food-rich micro-habitat. It was shown, for example, that a stackyard comprising six ricks could attract a population of both rats and mice during March collectively numbered at 1,200 individuals. Of the 605 rats which were present, more than 30% were below 44 g body weight and 50% below 95 g (Venables and Leslie 1942). This would have provided a potential prey population of around 1,000 small commensal rodents, largely confined within the limits of a single yard, their zone of activity determined only by the accessibility of nearby water. The Bank Vole *Cletherionmys glareolus*, Wood Mouse *Apodemus sylvaticus*, and Harvest Mouse *Micromys minutus* were also species which were attracted to these ricks and like the rat, reproduction could be maintained throughout the winter season (Frank 1957).

Other indications of the high rodent density in the days of the rickyard can be obtained from the numbers of Brown Rats killed and recorded by gamekeepers (Twigg 1975). For example, in 1903 a single keeper on one estate in East Anglia killed 14,662 rats. In 1926, over 10,000 were killed, but by 1942 following the introduction of the combine harvester and the disappearance of the corn-rick, the number of rats decreased to 1,500 per annum even though keepering pressure on this estate remained constant. The last estimate in 1966 was 466 rats. Today, farmers in the single enterprise farming regions in parts of Lancashire and Eastern England rarely report seeing rats on their farms.

To the farmer of the early 1900s, the rickyard's other most obvious wildlife feature was the presence of huge wintering flocks of seed-eating birds attracted by the artificially provided food supply. From a more scientific viewpoint, the ecological importance of the corn-rick during the mid-1900s to sparrows, finches and buntings has also been emphasised (O'Connor and Shrubb 1986).

The diversity and abundance of suitable prey species once available to the Barn Owl in the old farmyard was therefore without question. Contemporary writers have described this owl 'as the police of the stackgarth' (Hancock 1874) and 'so tame they would pounce on the mice whilst the men were engaged in threshing'

(Bucknill 1900). The noted ornithologist, Lord Lilford, describing the Barn Owl's particular relationship with the rickyard at the turn of the century says, 'this was the Owl's special hunting ground, as I repeatedly observed: mice were comparatively scarce, probably because rats swarmed, and the pellets found under the nest were in this instance composed entirely of the remains of the latter vermin. In other cases, besides the above-mentioned account, I have found many skulls of Sparrows and Finches, which I presume were caught in the ricks' (Lord Lilford 1895).

Commensal rodents, perhaps not surprisingly, appear to have been far more important in the diet of the Barn Owl in the earlier part of this century than they are today. Collinge's study in economic ornithology (1924-1927), shows that the Brown Rat and House Mouse constituted about 58% of the diet by weight. Later, Ticehurst (1935) found that these farm rodents collectively comprised 43% of the bird's nutritional requirements. Even allowing for some sampling bias towards eastern England and the Midlands in Collinge's study these two commensals were clearly an important food source at this time.

During the Agricultural Research Council's study itself, Barn Owls were shown to be one of the major predators at infested ricks, not only hunting the barn floor and surrounding areas, but also nesting most commonly in the tunnel which often ran at eaves level for cooling purposes. Although no comprehensive study was made of pellet remains, at the one site they were analysed rats constituted approximately 80% of the prey species.

Historically then, the rickyard provided the Barn Owl with a rich alternative reservoir of food, peaking during the critical winter and early spring months, at precisely the time it was most needed to maintain survival and ensure optimal fertility and egg-laying success.

As we have seen, the rapid introduction of the combine harvester into Britain in the early 1940s meant that the storage and preservation of corn within unthreshed stacks no longer became necessary and, almost overnight, the corn-rick disappeared from the farming scene after a long history. It was, however, the timing of the sudden loss of this important prey-rich habitat which would have been so devastating to the Barn Owl population, since it coincided with the start of the worsening winters of the 1940s, when the pressures for an alternative and dependable winter food source would have become even more acute. Had the corn-rick remained a feature of our farmland, then it seems improbable that there would have been such a major change in the Barn Owl population in the British Isles, in spite of the continued worsening of the winter climate.

Figure 10 indicates the increase in harvesting mechanisation in Britain. This mirrored the equally rapid disappearance of the corn-rick and serves to illustrate both the timing and rapid rate of loss of this important foraging habitat for the Barn Owl. The steep decline in

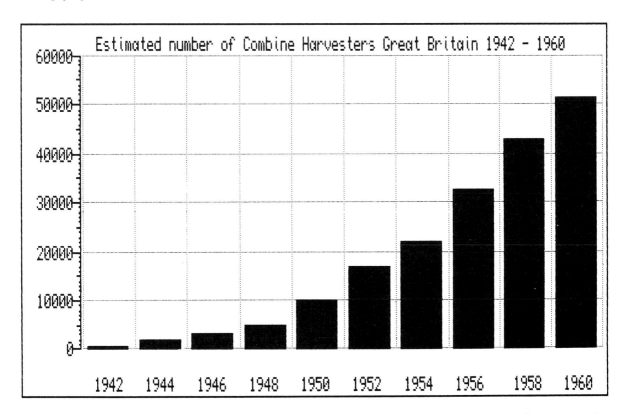

Fig. 10 **Biennial estimate of the number of combine harvesters in use in Great Britain 1942–1960 (HMSO 1968).**

The introduction of the combine harvester in the early 1940s resulted in the disappearance of the corn-rick from most farms by the mid-1950s.

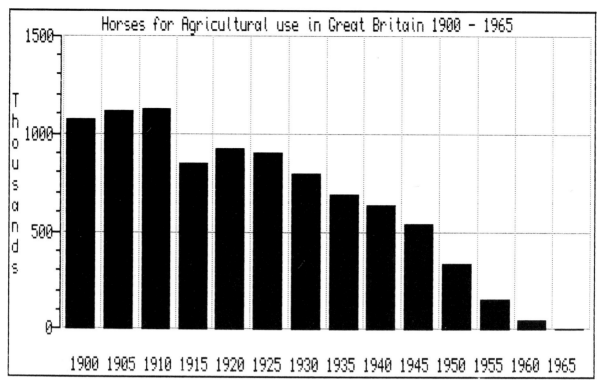

Fig. 11 *Quinquennial estimate of the number of horses (including mares for breeding) kept for agricultural use in Great Britain 1900–1965 (HMSO 1968).*

The substitution of animal draught by mechanised traction resulted in the demise of the working horse, together with straw-bedded stables, hay lofts and winter fodder stores. Like the corn-rick these prey-rich micro-habitats had therefore largely disappeared from farms by the mid-1950s.

the use of the working horse soon after the introduction of the tractor during the First World War, intensified in the depression of the 1920s and 1930s (Figure 11). As a result, the need for large winter fodder stores, stabling and straw-bedded animal yards largely declined by the 1950s, further reducing the foraging opportunities for the Barn Owl.

In assessing the importance of an alternative food source to the Barn Owl, it is perhaps significant that the present *Survey* has shown the bird's continued presence in winter at farm buildings where straw, hay or other food stuffs are stored. This is especially true throughout most of eastern Britain and in much of the North where winter severity and a shortage of grassland foraging areas in cereal dominated regions combine to reduce an already depleted prey source.

Corn for human consumption is now protected in rodent-proof bins or silos and most rodent infestations are confined to those more open barns containing hay, root crops or other animal fodder. As rodents and small birds centralise their foraging activities around these places, they in turn continue to provide the Barn Owl with an opportunity to feed, thereby offering a buffer against winter starvation. This is borne out by an examination of pellet samples collected from eighteen sites throughout Britain over the snowiest winters of the *Survey* period in 1985 and 1986. Pellet contents consistently revealed a very high proportion of less characteristic prey species such as House Mouse, Brown Rat, House Sparrow *Passer domesticus* and Starling *Sturnus*

vulgaris. Other birds and small insects constituted the entire content of many pellets. The sites from which they were collected further confirmed that Barn Owl survival continues to be highly dependent upon the continued presence of open barns, food stores, and over-wintering livestock pens on modern farmland.

Present prey populations around most farmsteadings rarely equal those provided by the old rickyard. In the cereal dominated expanses of eastern and central southern England, the lack of stock means that there is little need for permanent pastures or the storage of animal feeds. Consequently, even the once traditional hay barn has become less common here than in the pastoral South-west.

Habitat analysis suggests that the proximity of woodland is also an important habitat feature especially in winter. The presence of mature forest adjacent to open farmland and young plantations may take on additional significance, with the sheltered rides and leeward edges of the woodland providing the only opportunity of locating prey during prolonged snows.

In 1932 the cereal farming regions of central and eastern England were shown to hold the highest Barn Owl densities of between 10-20 pairs per 100 km^2. As a result of the major changes which have occurred in the storage of cereals, coupled with the worsening winters over the last fifty years, these regions have now experienced the most dramatic decline. Population levels are now averaging only 0-5 pairs per 100 km^2. Densities in many of these areas must now be considered critical.

It is the loss of this important winter food supply which began in the late thirties, at a time when the winters themselves were showing a worsening trend, that has been largely responsible for the widespread decline of the Barn Owl in the British Isles.

In Summer

Having dealt with the implications of a reduced food supply in winter, it must be remembered that throughout most of the year the Barn Owl is a bird of open land, depending mainly on the Short-tailed Vole and shrew. Indeed it is predominantly the abundance of these two small mammals which critically determines the bird's ultimate fledging success at a time during the breeding season when food demands can escalate to around thirty small mammals per day. Habitat quality is therefore of supreme importance to the Barn Owl, having to provide, in addition to adult needs, between 1,500–2,000 prey items over a twelve week period to enable the birds to rear four young succesfully. This protracted fledging period and its accompanying high prey requirement is unique in British birds of prey.

The vole and shrew are themselves dependent on tussocky grassland to provide them with food, shelter and nesting sites. Hedgerow, ditch, bank, woodland edge and marsh, together with the ploughed grassy furrows traversing young forestry plantations attract some of the highest small mammal densities. The foraging activities of the Barn Owl are not unnaturally concentrated around these field edges. Hedgerow timber and boundary posts make these grassland margins additionally attractive, allowing the Barn Owl an alternate means of 'still hunting'. This becomes important for maintaining hunting efficiency during periods of wet or gusty weather when the more normal methods of aerial quartering are less easily applied.

The disappearance of grassland edge particularly along hedgerows, ditches and banks coupled with the decline and changing management of grassland, has been considerable since the early 1940s following the dissolution of the mixed enterprise farm. The loss of these important foraging grounds has been predominantly at the expense of cereal intensification in the midland, eastern and central southern counties, maturation of commercial forestry in much of Wales, northern England and Scotland, and to some extent increased stocking rates elsewhere in the counties of north Lancashire, Cheshire, Staffordshire, Dorset and Avon. The disappearance of linear grassland features has therefore been greatest in these regions of single enterprise farming where crops now dominate 75-95% of agricultural land use or where stocking densities are the highest in the British Isles at between 50-70 livestock units per 100 acres (40 ha) of farmland. (Livestock units represent the sum of all classes of livestock weighted according to their grassland food requirements (Coppock 1976)).

The cereal regions of East Anglia, the East Midlands and the South-east.

In the cereal regions, hedgerows have been reduced in both extent and quality as large modern harvesting machines have demanded larger fields in which to operate. The disappearance of stock from farms in these areas has also reduced the need for enclosure. Underground drainage has, with the important exception of the Fenlands, largely replaced open ditch. In 1947, the total length of hedgerow, wall, bank and ditch stood at 6.9 km per square kilometre of non-urban land throughout the major cereal growing areas. Today it has declined to 5.3 km, a loss of 23% (Hunting Surveys 1986), and much of the remaining hedgerow has been reduced to a remnant of close-cropped stumps providing poor habitat for small mammals. The overall result is that the only areas within these regions which are not now under tillage are those confined to the river valleys and coastal marshes where crop growing cannot easily be increased without expensive drainage operations.

The specialised cattle-rearing areas of the North-west.

In the highly intensive stock-rearing areas, particularly in Cheshire and Staffordshire, wire fences have been constructed at the expense of hedgerow such that the length of this new form of enclosure has increased 30% since 1947, to 3.2 km per km^2 (Hunting Surveys 1986). Wire fencing and closely grazed pastures do not provide suitable vole or shrew habitat as tighter grazing and trampling of the sward destroys the tussocks.

Hay and straw are a very rare commodity here, where high rainfall makes hay-making difficult. Silage generated from heavily mown temporary grassland provides the major food source for cattle. Open concrete yards, wooden floor slatting and sawdust provide the usual 'bedding' materials. As a consequence of these very hygienic farming methods, commensal rodents, like small field mammals, are rarely observed. Not surprisingly the Barn Owl has become very scarce throughout this region too.

The mixed farming regimes of the South-west.

Although stocking rates have also increased to some extent in the South and South-west, good quality stock-proof hedges and banks remain intact in these more traditionally farmed regions. Here small fields provide sheltered and controlled grazing and remain well suited to livestock. The less specialised nature of farming here also means that between 25-50% of land is under tillage. Individual farm holdings are relatively small averaging between 20-300 acres (8-120 ha) whilst in the eastern and central-southern regions they are commonly 500-1000 acres (200-400 ha). In 1947 the length of linear features in the south-west region was 12.6 km/km^2. Today this has changed little at 11.3 km/km^2, a loss of only 10% (Hunting Surveys 1986). This suggests that field sizes here are a tenth of those in the eastern and central-southern regions where Barn Owl abundance is now low (Coppock 1976).

The diverse farmland habitats of the South-west therefore continue to maintain extensive lengths of rough grassland edge and so still provide some of the best Barn Owl habitat in the British Isles.

The Effects of a Loss in Habitat Continuity

One of the most significant causes of the widespread decline of the Barn Owl throughout the British Isles has been the erosion and eventual loss of grassland continuity. Intensive and specialised agriculture, particularly in those regions described above, has largely destroyed the rough grassland dispersal networks where prey was once freely available. These networks were provided by riverside, hedgerow and small pastures which inter-linked prime habitats and permitted the successful interchange of young birds. Although farm and estate lands in some areas still remain admirably suited, the sheer vulnerability of these isolated breeding colonies means that even from many apparently ideal habitats, the Barn Owl has now disappeared.

SECONDARY CAUSES

Roadway Development and Urbanisation

The road network in the British Isles has expanded rapidly since the 1950s, stimulated by mounting traffic densities and demands for faster travel. In Britain our highways now cover more than 164,000 miles (Secrett and Cliff Hodges 1986) with motorway and trunk road construction dominating both the urban and rural scene. Urbanisation and associated developments have been responsible for the loss of one million hectares (about 8.5%) of agricultural land over the last sixty years (Best 1976, 1977). This has led to localised Barn Owl decline in the vicinity of expanding towns. New and improved road networks not only account for the erosion and fragmentation of once traditional type habitats but also result in unprecedented levels of Barn Owl fatality.

It is tempting, therefore, to draw the conclusion that the increasing proportion of road deaths seen today is a primary cause of the bird's declining numbers. Whilst it is undeniable that the number of Barn Owl road victims has at least doubled since the mid-1950s to about 5,000 per annum, it remains debatable whether or not this unnatural cause of mortality is contributing to any major increase in death rate or is simply replacing some other more natural cause.

What is without doubt, however, is that a much higher level of fatality does occur in those areas where major roads are straightened or improved or where new motorways and bypasses are constructed through other-wise prime habitat. Motorway construction, for ex-ample, not only consumes upwards of twenty-six acres of farmland per mile but often results in the splitting up of traditionally farmed landscapes with their complex field, ditch and hedgerow patterns. This not only results in the direct loss of suitable habitat but exposes the birds to the hazards of fast-moving traffic on the newly created foraging grounds provided by the roadside verges.

As well as establishing the current level of road mortality, the present *Survey* results indicate that following the opening of new motorways, mortality becomes very high over the first five to ten years, after which casualty numbers fall off as local populations become rapidly depleted. For the older, more established motorways, such as the M1 and M4, few casualties are now reported. Indeed, habitat analysis confirms that less than 0.5% of the breeding population in the British Isles now nests within 1 km of any motorway. Analysing this still further, less than 2% are within 3 km, the distance generally considered to be the limit of the bird's hunting range. Where Barn Owls continue to be found nesting close to motorways, it is perhaps significant that this generally concerns the more recently constructed sec-tions where presumably local populations have not yet become entirely depleted.

Certainly, Barn Owls are commonly reported hunting roadsides even in situations where prime water meadow habitats exist alongside. What then makes these roadside hunting grounds so attractive? Quite simply the estab-lished linear grasslands provided by the roadside edge support high densities of prey. Small mammals thrive in these undisturbed and unmanaged grasslands. Perhaps even the increased warmth emitted by passing vehicles results in an extended growing season for grasses thus providing a more hospitable micro-habitat to voles and other small animals especially during winter. Frequently during periods of heavy snowfall or frosts the salt-loaded verges continue to provide exposed grassland over which the birds can forage. Additionally, whilst hedgerow and ditch have largely disappeared on farmland, they often remain intact adjacent to roadsides. Here, hedgerows and boundary posts provide opportunities for 'still hunting' particularly during bad weather. In some counties, especially those in eastern England, where the more natural hunting grounds on farmland have largely disappeared, the wide roadside verges and adjacent hedgerows provide the only grassland remnants.

From the mortality study conducted, it can be seen that the highest death rate occurs in the late autumn and winter period following fledging in September. A considerable proportion of casualties are first year birds. Numerous recorders reported multiple deaths during the months of September, October and November on single stretches of road, sometimes on the same day and often within a week or month of one another.

The joint findings of the *Survey* would indicate that to the Barn Owl, roadside edges constitute a most impor-tant dispersal network for young inexperienced birds as they follow these prey-rich corridors in an attempt to establish new territories away from their natal areas. However, whilst roadside hunting may contribute to the Kestrel's survival, these attractive grassland corridors constitute hazardous hunting grounds for the Barn Owl with the result that local extinction can occur rapidly following highway development. Indeed, this modern form of human destruction may soon be approaching the level of that which occurred from persecution in the nineteenth century.

The Loss of Nest Sites and Increased Human Activity

As this *Survey* has already shown, nest site selection by the Barn Owl varies markedly from region to region. Throughout the southern and western seaboard coun-ties, where annual rainfall is high, the birds select almost exclusively the more sheltered man-made structures, whilst in the drier East, trees are the favoured nesting site. Clearly such findings are of prime importance when considering the relevance of nest site loss to this species.

For example, the increasing reduction of old agricul-tural buildings in the South-west might seriously affect population levels, whilst the loss of hollow trees in this region is unlikely to take on major importance. In the east of Britain, however, the disappearance of trees would be of far greater significance; whilst in the midland counties, where the bird selects both man-made and tree sites equally, the decline of either type of site might be expected to influence Barn Owl numbers.

For many years it has been believed that a prime cause

Fig. 12

Comparison of Nest Site Selection in England and Wales in 1932, with that Observed Today

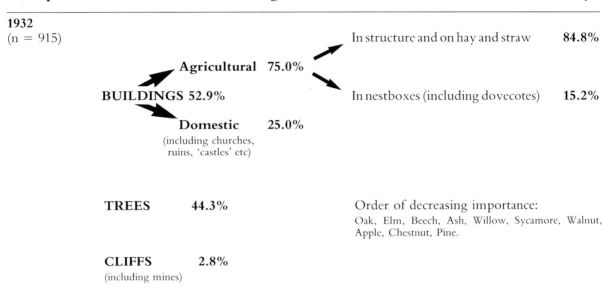

1932
(n = 915)

BUILDINGS 52.9%

Agricultural **75.0%**

Domestic **25.0%**
(including churches,
ruins, 'castles' etc)

In structure and on hay and straw   **84.8%**

In nestboxes (including dovecotes)   **15.2%**

TREES   **44.3%**

Order of decreasing importance:
Oak, Elm, Beech, Ash, Willow, Sycamore, Walnut,
Apple, Chestnut, Pine.

CLIFFS   **2.8%**
(including mines)

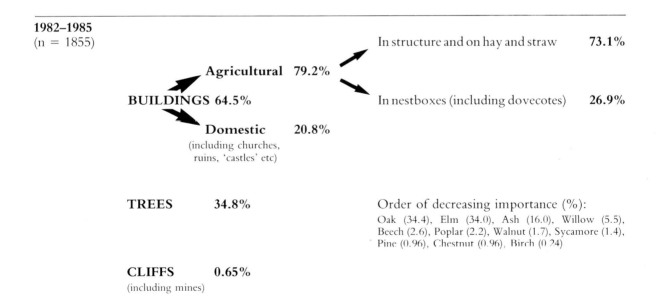

1982–1985
(n = 1855)

BUILDINGS 64.5%

Agricultural **79.2%**

Domestic **20.8%**
(including churches,
ruins, 'castles' etc)

In structure and on hay and straw   **73.1%**

In nestboxes (including dovecotes)   **26.9%**

TREES   **34.8%**

Order of decreasing importance (%):
Oak (34.4), Elm (34.0), Ash (16.0), Willow (5.5),
Beech (2.6), Poplar (2.2), Walnut (1.7), Sycamore (1.4),
Pine (0.96), Chestnut (0.96), Birch (0.24)

CLIFFS   **0.65%**
(including mines)

of the Barn Owl's decline has been the reduction of suitable nest sites as a consequence of the decay or modernisation of farm buildings together with the disappearance of old trees through over-maturity, disease and hedgerow clearance. Whilst the accelerating loss of these sites between 1950 and 1980 has been undeniable, the *Survey* has identified little major change in the relative proportions of buildings and trees being used as nest sites in England and Wales since 1932 (Figure 12). The small loss (9%) of tree sites which appears to have occurred over this period can simply be accounted for by the disproportionate decline of the Barn Owl from eastern regions where trees have always been the favourite nest site. The lack of change in relative usage between these two major classes of nest site over the last fifty years suggests that neither site has yet become limiting.

Indeed, there appear to be few counties, with the exception of those in the Fenlands of East Anglia, where the numbers of potentially suitable, but hitherto un-occupied nest sites, are not in excess of the present breeding population. This includes many traditional Barn Owl sites which although intact nevertheless remain unoccupied.

The general availability of sites can also be demon-strated from a local field study conducted by the author in Hertfordshire, a county where the population has declined to unprecedented levels since 1932. In this county, the population is less than 10 pairs and has been at low levels since the 1960s. However, in the 100 km² area selected for study which now contains just one pair of owls, as many as twenty-five potentially suitable nest sites were available, many in derelict pigeon lofts of barns, as well as an additional twenty-eight vacant tree cavities. This represents a total of over fifty sites, one for every 2 km². In addition, almost every farm in this surveyed area contained a bale stack providing a further potential nesting site of the type most commonly used in agricultural buildings nationally. Consultation with other Barn Owl specialists in central-southern, midland and eastern regions confirmed that the numbers of potential nest sites appear to exceed the present Barn Owl breeding population in their county many times over, indicating that the habitat surveys in Hertfordshire are likely to be representative in this respect.

The number of artificial sites which have been provided for this bird, in the form of barrels and nestboxes, can currently be estimated at between 50-200 for almost every county in England and Wales. Barrels were advocated for the Barn Owl as early as 1894 (Robinson). The total number of artificial sites now probably exceeds 6,000 – equivalent to one for every remaining Barn Owl pair. Whilst some may have been inexpertly sited, there is little reason to blame inadequate design for their general lack of occupancy. The same style of box is readily used when placed at existing nest sites in favour of the traditionally used ledge or crevice (Moss pers. comm; Orchel pers. comm). In spite of the vast excess of artificial as well as natural sites available, the provision of nestboxes appears to have done little to stabilise breeding numbers and arrest the overall popu-lation decline in Britain.

Increased human activity can also prevent birds from selecting otherwise suitable roosting and nesting sites.

This need for seclusion probably accounts for the fact that 39% of nest sites in barns are to be found on or within hay and straw. It could be supposed that increased human disturbance has led to the birds selecting these secluded sites more commonly in recent years. How-ever, as long ago as 1932, Blaker ranked this second in his listing of the type of barn site used and even then nest sites in hay were probably subject to an equal degree of disturbance, since most ricks had been threshed and dismantled by June, giving the birds little opportunity to fledge successfully.

The Barn Owl's fidelity to traditional nesting sites, and more importantly to the prey-rich habitats which surround them, is very strong until such time as alteration or disturbance reaches an intensity which threatens successful nesting. Clearly, a large proportion of Barn Owls are displaced each year and forced to find new breedings places. Even assuming they are reluctant to breed elsewhere, younger birds should be capable of maintaining population levels given that other potent-ially suitable sites are available in the area. Indeed, whilst many traditional nest sites have been used for decades, the loss and creation of sites has occurred regularly throughout history.

The *Survey* has established little evidence for the commonly held belief that the loss of nest sites is a primary cause of the species' decline nationally. Rather it has again reinforced the findings that grassland foraging habitat has been depleted and fragmented at an alarming rate and that this together with worsening winters is of primary significance.

Insecticides and Rodenticides

The detrimental effects of certain industrial and agricultural chemicals on non-target wildlife have featur-ed prominently in the decline of many predatory species. This followed the major changes in farming methods stimulated by the increasing need for self-sufficiency in food production during the Second World War. Today the populations of the majority of raptor species have substantially recovered from the effects of these chem-icals. The *Survey* has nevertheless identified a relatively new series of pesticides, the 'second generation' rodenti-cides, which since the author's initial concerns early in 1982 have been shown by chemical tests to be capable of causing mortality to wild Barn Owls. These are a potential threat to already fragile population levels. Before discussing this latest problem however, the impact of the earlier agricultural and industrial chemicals on Barn Owl numbers between the mid-1940s and the late 1970s will be reviewed.

Bird casualties began to appear in Britain on an increasingly large scale from 1952 soon after the introduction of the organophosphorus insecticides in the mid-1940s (Moore 1965). This group of pesticides was followed immediately afterwards by the organochlorine chemicals which began with the introduction of DDT in 1945. The insecticide was used primarily in preventing damage to standing crops such as cereals, brassicas and orchard fruits. In 1955 a new class of organochlorine, the cyclodienes, was introduced, the most important of which were aldrin, dieldrin and heptachlor. Unlike DDT, the cyclodienes were used mainly to combat a multitude of different soil pests such as wheat bulb fly, carrot fly and wireworms and as such were predominantly applied as a seed and root dressing to cereals, brassicas and potatoes. In addition, dieldrin was used in sheep dips to protect against fly strike.

DDE is the major degradation product of DDT in animals, whilst HEOD is the active ingredient of dieldrin and the product of aldrin metabolism. All three of these organochlorines and in particular DDT are highly persistent in the environment (many decades in the case of DDT) and in animal tissues, especially fat. It is this fat-solubility coupled with their prolonged persistence which allows these chemicals to systematically ascend the food chain, via the smaller prey species, eventually concentrating in the tissues of predatory and scavenging birds. Whilst predators of seed-eating birds were considered to be at higher risk, the wide distribution of these chemical residues in soil, water and on foliage has also resulted in serious contamination of small mammal feeders.

DDT, and its breakdown product DDE, are in fact of low direct toxicity to birds. High residues however, can cause poor breeding success due to egg-shell thinning, consequent egg breakage and embryo death. These potentially serious sub-lethal effects are believed to take on major significance when liver residues contain 10 parts per million (ppm) or more of DDE, whilst death itself is only attributed to levels exceeding 100 ppm. HEOD unlike DDT does however cause direct toxicity and there is general agreement that the level necessary to cause death is 10 ppm or above.

In 1956, a year after the introduction of aldrin and dieldrin, severe bird casualties were once again observed and it was from this period that a noticeable decline in the numbers of birds of prey began, coinciding with the widespread use of organochlorine pesticides in agriculture. In the British Isles, the first reported Barn Owl incident which was thought to have involved one of these chemicals occurred in 1960, followed in 1961 by an additional case and in 1962 by no less than eighteen further incidents. Whilst residue analyses were not conducted on all of these specimens, half were shown to contain organochlorine residues in the range 0.3-3.0 ppm, and all but one of these birds originated from the eastern regions of England. In one further specimen from Kent, the level was as high as 11.9 ppm and it was perhaps significant that both Tawny Owls and Little Owls *Athene noctua* from this county also demonstrated the highest dieldrin levels of the six species of bird of prey analysed at this time (Cramp 1963).

In 1965, the results of an NCC study (Moore 1965) were reported. Tissue levels of organochlorines in six Barn Owl carcases ranged between less than 0.1 ppm to 5.0 ppm whilst in an additional two specimens, residues were 7.0 and 20 ppm. Although it could not positively be concluded at the time that these levels were high enough to have actually caused the death of the birds, it indicated that significant residues were now accumulating in this species.

At about the same time, an enquiry was mounted to assess the extent of changing numbers of Britain's smaller birds of prey and corvids (Prestt 1965). This study which included the Barn Owl, sought largely subjective opinions related to the extent of population change between the years 1953-1963. Opinions were extracted from 141 completed questionnaires received from a wide cross-section of the general public. These included countrymen and ornithologists, many of whom would have been already aware that a decline associated with toxic chemicals was occurring.

The findings of the enquiry were far from clear-cut and although it was concluded that the Barn Owl had undergone a general decline, in no region was it considered to have been 'very marked'. Respondents were equally divided about the nature of the decrease, some believing it to have been long-term, whilst others considered it a more recent and perhaps temporary change. In most of the eastern regions, including Kent, together with the northern counties of England, the Isle of Man, Hampshire, Dorset and Somerset, there did however emerge more consistent reports of a decrease in numbers. The reasons given for this general decline were once again by no means unanimous, with pesticides actually coming second to the combined loss of habitat and food supply in the scoring system used to determine the relative importance of the possible contributory causes.

The Barn Owl's decline was reported to have become most apparent after 1958. This, as we know, was a year of climatic extreme and even today remains the wettest spring/summer season on record since 1927. In 1958 there were also reports of very low populations of small mammals. Both factors contributed to the poorest breeding season known for the Tawny Owl (Southern 1959) and the Barn Owl (Figure 3). Not only was 1958 a year of high rainfall but it was followed by the increasingly hard winters of 1962 and 1963, the latter noted for its unprecedented severity this century, when 63 days of snowcover were recorded. It is also significant that the worsening climate was given as one reason for the species' temporary change in status by respondents to this enquiry.

'In striking contrast to the previous species, the Tawny Owl was remarkable for its lack of change during the period' (Prestt's words). In spite of this owl's not dissimilar prey preferences, its stability perhaps reflected the species' greater resistance to what was already a long-term deterioration in the climate.

Whilst this particular study therefore served to indicate some decline in Barn Owl numbers from the secondary effects of organochlorine pesticides, in retrospect it now becomes tempting to conclude that once again climate may have played the major part in the bird's decline between the years 1953-1963.

The most important long-term pesticide monitoring study was that conducted at the Institute of Terrestrial Ecology, Monks Wood between 1963 and 1977 (Cooke *et al*, 1982). This involved sixteen species including the Barn Owl and body tissues were analysed for residues of DDE, HEOD, PCB (an industrial contaminant chemically similar to DDT) and mercury (a seed fungicide). The final conclusions of this study were in the main supported by those of a separate long-term investigation by the Pest Infestation Control Laboratory, Ministry of Agriculture, Fisheries and Food, (Stanley and Elliott 1976; Cooke *et al* 1982). The total number of Barn Owl specimens analysed by ITE over this period amounted to 251.

Pesticide residues generally appeared to be consistently

higher during early spring particularly in Barn Owls of lower than average body weight, probably due to the mobilisation of residues from fat as this became depleted during late winter. Barn Owls showed greatest DDE residues in the south-east of England and a general increase in contamination during the 1960s averaging around 1.0 ppm. After reaching a small peak between 1967 and 1969, levels of DDE then decreased slowly throughout the 1970s. HEOD residues were highest in the main wheat bulb fly areas of eastern England, north of the Thames, and in the Isle of Man, fluctuating around an overall mean of 1.0 ppm between 1963-1977 with some slight tendency to decline from a small peak in 1973. PCB residues, unlike DDT and HEOD, showed no regional trend. A marked decrease was recorded just prior to their partial withdrawal by the manufacturers in 1971. Mercury levels dropped significantly between 1970 and 1975 from 0.5 to 0.2 ppm without any restrictions having been imposed. Mercury levels tended once again to be highest in East Anglia, central southern England and the Isle of Man.

When all species were arranged according to their average contamination level of HEOD, Barn Owls and Kestrels appeared sixth and seventh in the ITE list and even during the period of peak residues, less than 19% of tissue samples indicated greater than 10 ppm. By 1977, Barn Owls were showing no major contamination from DDE, HEOD, PCB or mercury.

Whilst it could reasonably be concluded that some Barn Owls died as a result of direct poisoning by the cyclodienes, the effects DDE may have had on reproduction remain unknown since egg samples were not analysed for this species.

A voluntary ban on the use of aldrin, dieldrin and heptachlor began in 1961 but the purely voluntary nature of these agreements with manufacturers, distributors and users by no means led to their sudden disappearance from agriculture. Further restrictions were applied in 1965 and 1969 whilst dieldrin was banned from use in sheep dips in 1965. In 1971, PCBs were partially withdrawn by the manufacturers. It was not until December 1975 however, that dieldrin was withdrawn as a seed dressing although the use of DDT was actually believed to have temporarily increased at this time. In spite of further EEC restrictions in 1981, both aldrin and DDT continue to be used albeit on a much reduced scale.

In conclusion: whilst organochlorine insecticides were a major cause of the decline of many diurnal birds of prey in the late 1950s and 1960s, the Barn Owl would appear to have been much less affected.

Rodenticides have been implicated in the deaths of Barn Owls in Britain since the early 1930s (Wilson 1933). Blaker himself also considered that rodent poisons were contributing to the bird's decline in 1932; indeed he established that death in one specimen was attributable to phosphorus poisoning. Since the 1930s other literature references have appeared relating both Barn Owl and Tawny Owl decline to the secondary toxicity from rodenticides (Weir, Garrard in Bunn *et al* 1982). Although our current concerns are therefore nothing new, the major advances which have occurred in rodenticide technology since 1952 are such that these modern chemicals are vastly different in their chemistry, field application and potency from those which were more commonly used in the past.

Rodenticides are some of the earliest of pesticides. Aristotle described arsenic as a means of rodent control as early as 350 BC. In the eighteenth century, strychnine was widely applied and in the early 1900s thallium and barium salts appeared. Shortly afterwards, zinc phosphide was introduced and together with norbomide, alphachloralose and lindane (1960s), remain in continued use today.

Most of the chemicals so far described are acute mammalian stomach poisons, causing death after a single lethal dose within a few hours of ingestion. Reports of rodenticide toxicity in Barn Owls prior to 1952 would have involved acute poisons, death occurring as a consequence of feeding upon contaminated carcases or sublethally poisoned rodents. These chemicals resulted in almost instant death to rodents and because the Barn Owl is adverse to taking carrion would have probably reduced the opportunity for secondary poisoning. For this reason, acute poisons whilst causing some mortality are unlikely to have presented any major population risk to this species.

However, when endrin (an organochlorine developed as an insecticide) was used as a rodenticide against voles in Germany, eleven Barn Owls were subsequently found dead (Przygodda 1964). In diurnal birds of prey too, both strychnine and phosphorus rodent poisons have resulted in mortality, indicating that exposure to acute rodenticides via the secondary route is by no means unknown (Mullie and Meninger 1985).

In 1952, a revolutionary class of rodenticides appeared. They were known as anticoagulants and were based upon the natural poisonous substance in clover hay called coumarin. The synthetic poisons which were subsequently developed, although highly effective against rodents and generally much safer, were very slow acting in contrast to their acute predecessors. It was now necessary for a rodent to feed on a succession of daily doses of the bait before sufficient poison was consumed to cause internal haemorrhaging and eventual death. Often this would take between one and three weeks. Because death was no longer immediate these contaminated, sometimes lethargic rodents remained freely available to predators over a prolonged period.

Warfarin was the first and perhaps remains the most well known anticoagulant rodenticide of the coumarin type. This poison was followed by a large number of similar compounds including a series of anticoagulants known as indanediones. These, together with the coumarin poisons, soon became responsible for secondary poisoning in both domestic and wild species including birds of prey (Ashworth 1973). Even accidental human fatalities were recorded (Lange and Terveer 1954).

However, because warfarin, like others in its class, is of relatively low direct toxicity and is rapidly metabolised in mammals, owls would need to consume a relatively large quantity of contaminated prey over a period of many days to succumb to the effects of the poison. As far as warfarin is concerned, this is likely to require the consumption of more than 10 contaminated small mammals per day – far in excess of the bird's normal daily requirement. This relatively wide safety margin appears to be confirmed by field observations in

Malaysian oil palm plantations. There, warfarin-contaminated rats *R.tiomanicus*, *R.argentiventer* and *R.exulans* were freely available to Barn Owls following fairly regular baiting, yet in spite of heavy predation of these rodents there was little indication that secondary poisoning had occurred (Duckett pers.comm). Nevertheless, sub-lethal biochemical changes in blood have been observed in Tawny Owls fed warfarin-poisoned laboratory mice (Townsend 1981), suggesting that even warfarin has some potential to cause secondary poisoning in owls. It seems unlikely however that any significant level of mortality has occurred in wild Barn Owls as a result of these 'first generation' anticoagulants.

Soon after the introduction of warfarin, rats began to exhibit an increasing tolerance to this and other 'first generation' anticoagulants. By 1958 genetically acquired resistance to warfarin was confirmed in rats in the central lowlands of Scotland near Glasgow and soon after on the Anglo/Welsh borders in Montgomeryshire. Resistance in mice was then discovered near Harrogate. By 1966 this resistance had spread into central southern England around Reading and Basingstoke and into parts of the Kent Weald. Areas in Gloucestershire and South Yorkshire were similarly affected about this time and although resistance in rats was occurring in these well defined regions, in mice it had become countrywide by the late 1960s.

Tolerance by rats to these earlier compounds stimulated the development of new and more effective poisons. In 1974, difenacoum was introduced (registered 1975), the first of the 'second generation' anticoagulant rodenticides which could overcome this resistance factor, having a potency some 100 times greater than that of warfarin. In 1980, bromadiolone became available in the UK, demonstrating a slightly increased potency over its competitor, difenacoum. In 1984, brodifacoum was introduced for limited applications, having an activity about 600 times that of warfarin. It showed an increased potency and a persistence of some months in those mammals treated (Rammell *et al* 1984). Although all three of these new anticoagulants were substantially more potent, like warfarin, their delayed action remained unchanged. This now exposed predators to highly contaminated prey, over a prolonged period of one to three weeks.

The potential risk of secondary poisoning from these three 'second generation' rodenticides was first positively identified from laboratory trials in 1980. Poisoning was found to occur after feeding captive Barn Owls on rats contaminated with these compounds (Mendenhall and Pank 1980). Subsequently a similar trial involving Tawny Owls fed difenacoum-poisoned mice culminated in their death 8-14 days following initial exposure to the rodents (MAFF/ADAS 1982). A further laboratory trial involving Buzzards *Buteo buteo* fed on bromadiolone-treated voles (one vole per day for three days) resulted in the death of two of these birds. The chemical residues detected in the livers following post-mortem examinations were however below the limits of detection, suggesting that residue analysis may not be a useful indicator of secondary poisoning by bromadiolone (Grolleau and Lorgue 1984).

Rodent control in the UK is mainly confined to commensal rodents (rats and mice)in and around farm buildings. However, baiting also commonly occurs along hedgerows, especially during the autumn in an attempt to reduce the movement of rats into farm buildings in winter. This is also a common game management practice for protecting pheasant and partridge stock. Baiting in this way exposes the Barn Owl to a high risk from secondary poisoning since field margins constitute the primary hunting habitat for this species throughout most of the year, whilst farm buildings take on major significance in winter.

Difenacoum and bromadiolone have unrestricted use here in Britain under the Pesticide Safety Precautions Scheme and are freely available to the public for either agricultural or indeed household use. Brodifacoum, however, because of continued concerns from MAFF over its wildlife toxicity and persistence (especially in birds), continues to receive only 'provisional clearance' for use by professional operators (not farmers etc). However this does not prevent its use outdoors.

In 1982 in the Swiss canton of Neuchatel, following baiting with bromadiolone for the Northern Water Vole *Arvicola terrestris*, a serious incident occurred involving mass mortality of an estimated 185 Buzzards *Buteo buteo*, twenty-five Kites *Milvus milvus*, one Goshawk *Accipiter gentilis* and several predatory mammals. It was considered that this total was equivalent to, or higher than, the resident local population of the Buzzard and Kite although it was later believed that some migrants may have been involved (Pedroli 1983; Beguin 1983).

In Britain, one of the first indications of the hazards to wildlife posed by these 'second generation' poisons occurred following a baiting session with brodifacoum around a farmstead in a field trial region of Hampshire in 1981 prior to the compound's registration. Mass mortality occurred once again to a wide range of non-target wildlife including Tawny Owl, Buzzard, Magpie *Pica pica*, Pheasant *Phasianus colchicus*, Fox and even Hare *Lepus capensis*. Subsequent examinations of the specimens collected confirmed that death had occurred as a result of anticoagulant poisoning.

The Hawk Trust was already receiving unconfirmed reports of a sudden decline (estimated at around 90%) of Barn Owl numbers in 1981 following the recent replacement of warfarin with coumachlor and brodifacoum on an oil palm estate in Malaysia. Dead Barn Owls were now found frequently amongst the palms and in the majority of cases blood was apparent around the anterior nares, an indication of poisoning from anticoagulant rodenticides (Duckett 1984).

Screech Owl *Otus asio* mortality occurred in orchards in Virginia where brodifacoum was applied to control voles. Post-mortem examinations of one owl revealed extensive subcutaneous haemorrhaging on the lower breast extending around the hips and kidney. Other older intra-muscular clots were apparent on the legs. Analysis revealed the presence of brodifacoum residues and death was attributed to secondary poisoning by this rodenticide (Merson *et al* 1984).

However, research sponsored by ICI in New Jersey, USA concluded that the risk to Barn Owls from secondary poisoning was low because the bird's hunting range rarely overlapped with that of the contaminated rodents around farm buildings. Clearly this was not the situation in Malaysia, nor is it true for the British Isles

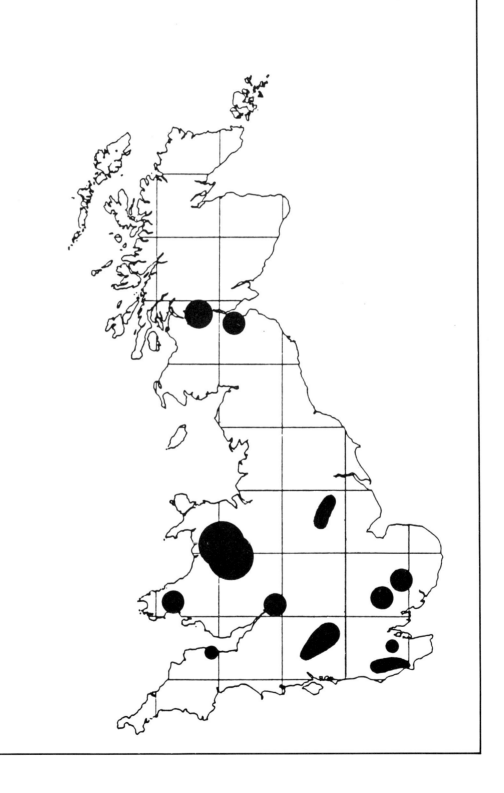

Map 12 **Centres of 'second generation' anticoagulant rodenticide usage.**

Barn Owls are especially vulnerable in these areas.

where Barn Owls are dependent for their over-wintering survival on the food and shelter provided by farm buildings, especially those containing hay or other food stuffs. Winter is the season when baiting most commonly occurs. It was perhaps not surprising therefore that in 1985, chemical tests carried out by DAFS (Department of Agriculture and Fisheries for Scotland) provided evidence that brodifacoum poisoning had resulted in mortality to a wild Barn Owl. Once again this bird originated from an area of Hampshire in one of the major centres of warfarin resistance.

The high potency of these 'second generation' compounds now suggests that, unlike warfarin, as few as 1-5 contaminated rodents may be sufficient to kill a Barn Owl (Shawyer 1985). This bird is perhaps at greatest risk in eastern England, the Isle of Man and Ireland, where commensals can range from 28-73% of the bird's diet by weight (Glue 1974; Smal 1987). However, even elsewhere, where rats and mice rarely constitute a major part of the annual diet, this owl continues to be at substantial risk especially during snow-covered winters when these rodents often become the only food available in and around farm buildings. Indeed it has recently been shown that rats also constitute as much as 25% of the autumn and winter diet of Barn Owls in Sussex (Shrubb 1984), and Glue (1967) has shown that when a drop in vole numbers occurred in a study area of Hampshire, Brown Rats took on increasing importance in the winter diet. Indeed there is little reason to doubt that elsewhere in the British Isles where cereal and root crop farming predominate, Brown Rats will provide a ready food supply. At a number of sites known to the author over 50% of the annual diet comprised rats. Bunn *et al* (1982) also report similar instances where pellet remains contained predominantly rats and mice.

Throughout the period of the present *Survey* reliable reports were received implicating rodenticides in Barn Owl mortality on farmland and in some cases around rubbish dumps. Rodenticide applications are no longer limited to indoor use and field baiting in hedgerows is becoming commonplace especially in autumn and early winter.

Provisional examination of carcases received revealed haemorrhaging on the lower breast and legs and in three cases around the beak and cloaca. Some of the fresher specimens were retained for further analysis. The majority of incidents were reported from the warfarin resistant areas, suggesting that the more potent 'second generation' rodenticides were involved. Information concerning those incidents where details were obtained is shown in Table 12. Whilst a further twenty cases were reported, these have not been included here because of their less informative nature, although the circumstances of death strongly suggested that rodenticides were implicated. Again, twelve of these specimens were retained for eventual analysis.

The specialised nature of the residue analysis for these rodenticides together with its cost and the difficulties of funding an independent analytical laboratory prepared to embark on this work, have so far precluded detailed chemical tests. However, in 1985 the author encouraged the NCC to provide a contract to ITE, Monks Wood to investigate rodenticide residues in owls.

Whilst it is very difficult to assess the extent to which rodenticides are contributing to the species' overall decline in the British Isles, in those areas of known anticoagulant resistance (north Hampshire, south Berkshire, Kent Weald, north Gloucestershire, Herts and other regions indicated in Map 12) the impact of these 'second generation' rodenticides appears of greater significance.

Barn Owl breeding numbers are now exceptionally low (0-2 pairs/ 100 km^2) in a narrow 15 km band between Wokingham (Reading/Berks) and the eastern outskirts of Salisbury (Wilts) which corresponds tightly with the defined region of highest 'second generation' usage, whilst just outside this zone, numbers remain especially high at 3-9 pairs 100 km^2. Data drawn from the Buckinghamshire and Hampshire bird clubs between 1967-74 (Warburton, compilation – county data 1972-1979) and distributional information of Barn Owl specimens received by MAFF during the period 1967-73 (Stanley and Elliott 1976) indicate an especially high density of Barn Owls within this zone until at least the mid-1970's.

It cannot be positively concluded that these potent rodenticides have been responsible for the dramatic decline of the Barn Owl in these regions. However, the time scale over which the decrease has occurred and the fact that field trials have been conducted with brodifacoum and its forerunners for over fifteen years, leading to incidents of wildlife mortality, lend support to the view that these chemicals have in some areas of the British Isles reduced Barn Owl populations.

Competition with the Tawny Owl

The Barn Owl was the most common owl at the beginning of this century but Blaker considered that the Tawny Owl had increased so rapidly since that time that their roles had been reversed throughout much of England and Wales by 1932.

Today the much more adaptable Tawny Owl is not only present in almost every municipal park, copse and woodland throughout mainland Britain but can also be found on more open farmland. Its expansion into this habitat over the last fifty years is now probably limited only by suitable nesting sites. The current population of the Tawny Owl has been placed in the range of 10,000-100,000 pairs. Its numbers are undoubtedly towards the upper limit of this range suggesting that the Tawny Owl is now probably about 15-20 times more common than the Barn Owl.

As the Tawny Owl has adapted to hunting on more open farmland and around farm buildings the Barn Owl has been forced into more direct competition, not only for food but perhaps also for tree-nesting sites. In situations where the Barn Owl commonly selects trees such as in central-southern and eastern England any competition of this nature is likely to take on greater significance. Reports suggest that the Barn Owl appears to have become more diurnal this century which may, in part, be in response to increased competition from the Tawny Owl as its numbers have expanded.

It has previously been reported that Tawny Owls will kill Barn Owls which compete for nesting sites (Kelsall and Munn 1905; Mikkola 1976). A few reports to the *Survey* involved Barn Owls which had been killed by Tawny Owls, usually near a tree nest site. Other reports more commonly concerned the latter species agressively dislodging Barn Owls and subsequently occupying these sites. This can also occur when captively reared Barn Owls are released into the wild from barn sites, presumably because they have been placed directly in Tawny Owl territories.

The Tawny Owl also selects its breeding site much earlier than other tree-nesting species. It is therefore capable of excluding Barn Owls, many of which will have vacated their trees during winter for more sheltered bale stack and farm building roosts giving the former owl the right of possession by default. Exclusion by the Grey Squirrel *Sciurus carolinensis* may also apply since it will commonly take over Tawny Owl sites, and those of Barn Owls where woodland is not far away.

Whilst it has already been shown that trees are usually only selected by Barn Owls for nesting in drier regions, it is interesting to note that on the Isle of Wight where climate is fairly moist and the Tawny Owl does not breed, 80% of Barn Owl nest sites are found in trees. One can only speculate whether the lack of competition here is partially responsible. However in Ireland where once again the Tawny Owl is a non-breeding bird, Barn Owls generally select old buildings in which to nest even though there is little competition for tree cavities.

The comparative success of the Tawny Owl since the early 1900s is probably due to its far greater adaptability during periods of harsh weather and food shortage. Unlike the Barn Owl, which remains a small mammal specialist, the Tawny Owl appears much better able to survive our changeable climate, switching successfully to earthworms during wet weather and bird prey during snow-covered winters, or indeed during any season. It is likely therefore that competition for food between these two species becomes more significant in areas where the Short-tailed Vole provides the main source of food.

However without specialised field work in selected areas, the significance of inter-specific competition between these two species remains largely unknown.

MORTALITY

No survey is complete, neither can a true assessment be made of the factors influencing population levels, without a firm understanding of the major causes of mortality. However, although it is possible to study and analyse both the type and extent of each of these causes, it is more difficult to interpret their individual importance in relation to a species' long-term decline.

Collision with road traffic, for example, can cause heavy annual mortality in certain avian species. Yet we could reasonably conclude that even in the absence of road deaths many of these birds would have died before attaining breeding age, entirely as a result of natural pressures. Additionally, whilst collision may have been the ultimate outcome, the stress caused by hunger may have been the primary factor which encouraged the birds to exploit these hazardous roadside hunting grounds; or alternatively perhaps because of their weakened state, the birds were ill-equipped to avoid the final collision.

A point must nevertheless be reached when the mortality caused by a man-made pressure reaches such high proportions that this pressure becomes a significant factor limiting a species' numbers, and as such, is partially or wholly responsible for a population decline. Human persecution, which led to the widespread decline of birds of prey in the nineteenth century, is an example of the way in which a single, unrelenting human activity can exact a heavy long-term toll on population levels.

The findings of any study designed to assess the relative importance of each of the factors responsible for mortality can clearly be influenced by the source from which the original information is gathered. Reports from taxidermists, for example, are likely to under-represent those birds which are shot, hung up on barbed wire or drowned, or indeed any other cause which may result in a specimen being unfit for mounting. Analysis of the ringing returns involving those specimens reported annually to the British Ringing Scheme administered by the BTO is also considered to demonstrate some degree of bias (Glue 1971).

In the case of the Barn Owl, bias is most likely to arise because the large majority of potential reporters to the BTO scheme are members of the general public who generally have restricted daily access to private farmland where a large proportion of these carcases are likely to be found. Furthermore, the majority of countrymen employed on the land have reported to the author that they rarely send in details of ringed owls or indeed any other birds found during the course of their work.

Before discussing the results of these investigations, it is important to consider the average annual death rate in numerical terms. With knowledge of the total breeding population, the breeding success rate and overall productivity in the British Isles, we can obtain a reasonable estimate of the annual mortality figure during an average year. From a total population of 5,000 pairs in Britain, and on the assumption that on average 70% breed successfully with a productivity of 3 fledged young per pair, we can see that 10,500 young birds are recruited into the population annually. However, since we also know that the population level is relatively stable from one year to the next (at least in the short term), then a total of 10,500 birds of varying ages must die each year to maintain the status quo.

The mortality investigations which follow encompass both Britain and Ireland and set out to determine the following:

(a) The relative importance of various causes of mortality.
(b) The months over which peak mortality occurred.

In order to provide the most meaningful statistics for these two mortality investigations, an attempt was made to select the reporting source relevant to the species itself and the particular analysis being performed. Of the 1,600 mortality records received during the period 1982-1986, 1,050 were of sufficient detail to allow precise interpretation of either the cause of death, the date of death or the sex of the specimen. Three distinct sources of data were used for this study: The Barn Owl Survey itself, where information of mortality was sought between 1983-1985; a special investigation which involved all 270 members of the Guild of Taxidermists (1982-1986); and data from The Hawk Trust's own post-mortem studies conducted by J.E.Cooper FRCVS supplemented by data kindly supplied by Dr.I.Newton of the Institute of Terrestrial

Ecology, Monks Wood, Cambridgeshire.

Causes of Mortality

Only the data supplied to the main *Survey* itself were used for this particular analysis. Working countrymen supplied 78% of the records, the remainder being provided by other informed members of the general public including ornithologists, both amateur and professional. A total of 629 records made up this group. Although an additional 228 records from taxidermy sources were available, these were rejected from this particular investigation in view of the likely bias in favour of the most easily found and undamaged specimens of which road victims were likely to have formed the bulk. Juvenile birds found 'dead at nest' although of very common occurrence were not included in any of the following analyses.

In the following categories of mortality, the percentage frequency of each cause is shown for England, Wales and Scotland (Figure 13). Ireland has been treated separately in this analysis (Figure 14).

Road Deaths 51.9% (n = 387)

This category includes all those Barn Owls which died as a result of a road accident involving lorries, vans and cars, and on occasion tractors and cyclists. The figure of 52% is a strikingly high proportion of the overall mortality. This is particularly interesting when one considers that the data used to compile this study were derived mainly from countrymen who not only travel the highways, but unlike many other sections of the reporting public, devote most of their working day to private farmland and its associated buildings, in situations where unusual carcases such as Barn Owls are less likely to be overlooked.

Previous studies (Glue 1971) using similar categories of mortality have shown that road deaths accounted for 6% (n = 7) of all recoveries between 1910-1954, with an increase to 15% (n = 31) between 1955-1969. Today, some twenty years later, the figure accounts for over half of the total mortality. Although some caution is needed in the interpretation of data derived from differing study designs, there is little reason to doubt that these percentages represent a fairly reliable picture of the increasing level of road deaths. (In the Netherlands road traffic was shown to account for 40.3% of known mortality – Braaskma and de Bruijn 1976). This increase has been brought about by the rise in numbers of faster vehicles, which together with major developments in trunk roads and motorway networks, have over the last two decades contributed to vastly increased traffic flows.

What then are the implications of this large road casualty figure? In absolute terms this would imply that 5,000 Barn Owls die annually on the road in Britain. In an attempt to substantiate this alarming figure, four sample regions were chosen as representative of England as a whole. Here specific requests were made to the public to notify all Barn Owl specimens found.

The first of these regions included 500 square kilometres centred around Woodbridge, where the public were asked to notify all specimens found during 1983 as part of a more extensive population census in Suffolk, co-ordinated by J.Martin. The second sample region comprised 200 square kilometres on the Selsey Peninsula

in West Sussex. Here repeated localised publicity was given for mortality records as a contribution to the main *Survey* during 1985. The third region encompassed 4,000 square kilometres around Norwich in Norfolk, where three taxidermists advertised their services during 1986. These individual sample areas returned annual road casualty figures of 25, 14 and 54 specimens. With the knowledge of the breeding population in each of these regions, it can be shown that road mortality accounted for 28%, 36% and 33% of the anticipated annual death rate which when extrapolated on a countrywide basis represents a total of 3,000 birds. This figure is however based only on those specimens actually notified in these regions and must be an underestimate of the actual numbers of Barn Owls killed. Nevertheless, we can now state with confidence that road casualties account for between 3,000 and 5,000 individuals per year in Britain and that the actual figure is more likely to approach the upper limit of this range. Even in the Republic of Ireland, a country where the volume of traffic is far less than elsewhere in the British Isles, road mortality constituted as much as 49% of all reported deaths between 1982-1986.

This major cause of mortality, must therefore, take on increasing importance in terms of population decline as the growth in traffic and associated road developments accelerate.

Two additional incidents of some general interest involved Barn Owls killed by combine harvesters. Although not strictly road incidents, one death occurred during night-time harvesting and the other under the mid-day sun. In both cases, the birds had been following the combine in the manner of Kestrels seeking small mammals dispersing from the stubble.

No Apparent Cause 23.2% (n = 173)

This classification refers mainly to those specimens found lying in fields and in open farm buildings showing no visible signs of any injury. Whilst this group may include a few birds which had previously flown into some object, and those which had succumbed to chemical poisoning, the large majority undoubtedly refer to Barn Owls which have died of starvation or some other natural cause. Care has been taken to exclude from this group birds which had died as a result of being trapped within buildings or those dependent young reported dead at nest.

Specimens reliably described as emaciated (n = 47) by veterinarians and other experts have been included in this category but have been distinguished in Figure 19 to illustrate those months during the year when starvation most commonly occurs.

The relationship of normal body weight to starvation level is now discussed briefly. Body weights were recorded for seventy-two freshly killed specimens of largely unknown sex and mixed-cause mortality. These birds were submitted to bird rescue centres, taxidermists and in response to The Hawk Trust's post-mortem investigations. Average body weight was 281.2 g. The highest weight registered was 389.2 g and the lowest 165.0 g. In the specimens weighing over 350 g between one to three recognisable prey items were present, partially digested in the gut, contributing to the overall weight.

Of the thirty-one carcases originating from healthy

birds (selected road casualties) the average body weight was 287.8 g. This is in agreement with the weights of all 97 road casualty specimens analysed by Hardy (1981), in which males averaged 281.6 g and females 297.4 g (av. 289.5 g). It has previously been reported by Piechocki (1960) that fat reserves are very low in Barn Owls *T. a. guttata* and that the starvation weight is 21% lower than in normal healthy specimens. This would suggest that starvation weight for *Tyto a. alba* would be about 227.4 g. It is nevertheless interesting to report that thirteen road casualty birds which were presumably still attempting to hunt up to the time of death, demonstrated body weights as low as 175-200 g.

It is worth noting that post-mortem investigations of a number of emaciated specimens revealed black tarry bile-like liquid in the gut. Presumably this is the fluid which would otherwise help bind the undigested prey remains giving the characteristic varnished appearance displayed by fresh Barn Owl pellets. At some roosts, large pools of a similar viscous black fluid could be found, either wet with the consistency of treacle, or as a hard dried shiny black pool, perhaps indicating periods of extreme hunger when insufficient food prevented these birds from casting solid pellets.

Drowning 6.16% (n = 46)

Drowning constitutes the second highest known cause of mortality in Barn Owls. This is most commonly found to occur in water butts, cattle troughs, tanks and slurry pits, but also in ponds, lakes, rivers and even the sea.

This apparent attraction to water is by no means unknown in owls and some very early records refer to Barn Owls dropping from a branch or skimming the water sometimes carrying off fish (Borrer 1891; Mitchell 1892; Balston *et al* 1907).

The first cumulative reports of drowning in Barn Owls were contained in the published results of Blaker's census where he stated, 'Nearly 40 such cases of drowning were brought to my notice and I have no doubt that there were many others. There was no specific sign of any violence upon them, except sometimes a wound in the region of the stomach, and no apparent cause of death except drowning'. In the early 1950s, and more recently, references have been made both in Britain and abroad, to owls drowning (Cameron Coulson 1950; Congreve 1950; Male 1950; Ryves 1950; Bunn *et al* 1982).

Many suggestions have been made as to its likely cause including thirst, attraction by the bird's own image and bathing. What is more certain however, is that Barn Owls become waterlogged within seconds of immersion (Ratcliffe pers.comm.), which reduces the bird's chances of escape especially from steep-sided containers where the depth of water is most probably misjudged at night.

The seasonal mortality pattern shown by Barn Owls may now provide some clue for this behaviour. Of the drowning reports received, 60% occurred in the month of July. This accounted almost entirely for the small but sudden peak observed in the seasonal mortality pattern during this particular month (Figures 15 and 18). Further, it would appear that this temporary peak is due entirely to female deaths; indeed, this is the only time during the year when any real difference in seasonal mortality between the sexes is observed.

The beginning of July coincides with the month during the breeding cycle when most females begin to emerge from the soiled confines of the nest site having incubated and brooded continuously throughout an eight-week period. It seems probable therefore, that drowning occurs as a result of unsuccessful bathing attempts to remove soiling and parasites after the prolonged nest confinement. Supportive evidence for this arises from studies with captive Barn Owls where it has been recognised that after brooding has been completed, the females leave the nestbox and immediately bathe, whilst at other times of the year this type of behaviour is unusual (Bunn *et al* 1982; Lewis pers.comm.; Sperring pers.comm.). Blaker's own observations of 'injury' to the breast of drowned specimens may more accurately refer to the remains of a brood patch, difficult to distinguish on waterlogged specimens, but again suggesting that drowning may be confined more specifically to female birds following brooding.

In five separate instances between 1982-1985 two or more birds were found drowned together, suggesting that family parties can also be involved. Three of these cases concerned water troughs during the period July – August and another occurred in a pond in October. Whilst water containers account for the majority of drowning incidents, Barn Owls have also been found alive but soaked in oil. It can only be presumed that these birds have attempted to bathe in open tanks of fuel oil or wood preservative, indeed at one forestry depot a Barn Owl was found floating in an open creosote tank.

Collision with Wires 5.09% (n = 38)

Overhead Wires

Flying into overhead wires represents a significant cause of mortality to Barn Owls at 3.4% (n = 25). Perhaps one of the earliest fatalities to a Barn Owl on telegraph wires was that reported by Stevenson and Southwell in Norfolk in 1866. Today, some fatalities may additionally occur by electrocution as a result of earthing on overhead power cables especially those serving the electrified rail network.

Fence Wires

Again, this is a relatively common hazard to Barn Owls on farmland 1.7% (n=13), although numerically many more casualties were recorded with Tawny Owls, probably a consequence of their larger numbers rather than their increased susceptibility. Most of the Barn Owl deaths in this category involved barbed wire and carcases were usually found hanging by the feet; no doubt the result of the bird's characteristic practice of dangling its legs in flight. Other casualties concerned those birds caught in fruit netting, chicken wire , a tennis net, and one which flew into a wired glass window has also been included in this category.

Trapped within Buildings 3.08% (n = 23)

This cause is self-explanatory. Most instances refer to Barn Owls which had fallen down a chimney into the rooms of houses left temporarily unoccupied. Commonly, these birds were also found having been inadvertently shut inside barns and warehouses or as a consequence of having been trapped within the roof space or ducting of commercial buildings. It seems that

TABLE 12

Rodenticide Incidents 1982–1985

Compound	Date	Place	No Barn Owls	Application	Situation Found	Operator	Observations
Difenacoum	12/82	Co. Tipperary	1	Farm Building	Inside Building	Farmer	Recovered following Vitamin K antidote.
Difenacoum	10/83	Newport I.O.W.	1	Field	Domestic Tip	Professional	Haemorrhaging beak and cloaca.
Difenacoum	2/84	Alford Lincs	2	Field	Potato Store	Farmer	Haemorrhaging at beak in one bird.
Difenacoum	11/85	Andover Hants	2	In Barn	In Barn	Farmer	Stoats and weasels also found dead.
Brodifacoum	5/84	Hawick Borders	2+1	In and around Barn	In Barn	Professional	Subcutaneous haemorrhaging in two birds.
Brodifacoum	2/85	Tarrant Hants	2	Barn and hedgerow	Outside farm buildings	Game-keeper	Subcutaneous haemorrhaging on legs and breast.
Brodifacoum	3/85	Andover Hants	1	Hedgerow	In farm-yard	Game-keeper	Haemorrhaging at beak.
Brodifacoum	1985	Whitchurch Hants	1	Outside farm building	Hedgerow	Game-keeper	Haemorrhaging.
Bromadiolone	2/85	Luton Beds	1	In and around foodstore	Outside foodstore	Professional	Subcutaneous haemorrhaging legs and breast.

the Barn Owl in its quest to find dark and secluded quarters in which to roost and nest suffers more from this cause of death than other species of owl.

Shooting and Trapping 2.68% (n = 20)

Inevitably, this cause of death is the one least likely to be reported and has, therefore, been much under-represented in studies of mortality, especially concerning those birds of prey protected by special penalties in law. Nevertheless, the noticeable downward trend from 12% of total reported mortality during the period 1910-1954, 5% between 1955-1969 (Glue 1971) to just 3% today, is encouraging. Whilst many keepers continue to persecute both Tawny Owls and Little Owls to some degree, the Barn Owl is today more highly regarded. So much so that on a number of private estates 'protection' from bird ringers is positively enforced. Whilst the nocturnal habits of owls reduce their chances of being shot, this not uncommonly occurs during wildfowling and pheasant shooting events usually as a result of mistaken identity! Although persecution remains of ethical concern, it is no longer of major conservation significance to the Barn Owl in Britain. In Ireland, however, it continues to take on greater importance with shooting representing 8% of notified mortality.

Detailed field studies in those regions where Barn Owl density is relatively high can however often indicate very obvious local gaps in the bird's distribution, demonstrating decisively those areas where persecution of the species continues to occur. Identification of these estates is a priority when targeting areas for conservation education.

Whilst the practice of pole-trapping was made illegal in 1904, and is now uncommon, bird of prey victims were nevertheless reported from a number of counties. Although these traps may be intended for other avian predators, Barn Owls also fall victim. Eight reported cases of pole-trapping were received during the *Survey* period.

Like other forms of human persecution, taxidermy has declined from its 'heyday' around 1880 when the majority of specimens were procured by trapping and shooting. Today, the ample supply of road casualties meets the current trade requirement. The demand for mounted Barn Owl specimens is now much reduced since the collecting era of the Victorian Age, and attitudes of the vast majority of taxidermists today (helped by the Wildlife and Countryside Act 1981), are such that specimens presented in suspicious circumstances are commonly rejected. All of which helps to further discourage the unlawful persecution of this bird.

In some areas of the Republic of Ireland, however, current attitudes toward the Barn Owl are much the same as they were in England a century ago. Although there has been some improvement, the Forest and Wildlife Service still considers taxidermy and shooting to be important causes of the species' continuing decline. It is perhaps significant that few Barn Owls in the Republic nest close to farmsteadings, tending to inhabit those more isolated, perhaps less vulnerable 'castles' and other derelict dwellings which today make up over 80% of all nest records from the country. In Northern Ireland, however, the Barn Owl is regarded in a somewhat different light and whilst shooting of this species continues, taxidermy is of less consequence.

Chemical Poisoning 3.22% (n = 24)

Extreme care has been taken to allocate to this category only those notified cases where the circumstances of death precluded any other obvious cause, the use of a named pesticide was heavy at the site of death or where other specimens were involved. The use of these stringent criteria undoubtedly leads to an underestimate of the mortality caused by chemical poisons. Nevertheless, the case histories given serve to demonstrate those classes of pesticide from which Barn Owls are particularly at risk, together with the regions where poisoning appears most prevalent.

Two major classes of pesticides have been implicated in Barn Owl mortality over the *Survey* period. Rodenticides accounted for 88% of reported poisoning incidents and molluscicides (slug and snail poisons) the remainder. The rodenticide incidents are summarised in Table 12. A more detailed account of the secondary effects of these poisons has been given previously.

Most reported incidents correspond with those regions where the potent 'second generation' anticoagulants, difenacoum, bromadiolone and brodifacoum are more commonly used (central southern England) or where commensal rodents form a major source of prey (Ireland, where poisoning accounted for 20% of total mortality, and eastern England).

Poisons were applied by professional operators, farmers and gamekeepers in farm buildings, commercial food stores and along hedgerows. Barn Owl corpses were usually found close to the baiting areas and most commonly within and alongside farm buildings, near potato dumps, rubbish tips and corn heaps provided for winter game feed. In the few cases when full details were available, owl corpses were found 8-25 days after baiting commenced. A number of incidents involved two or more birds usually found during the winter season between November and March, although one concerned an adult and two dead young in May. In one further incident, a Barn Owl recovered after administration of the vitamin K antidote by a veterinarian following a routine farm visit in Co Tipperary. The bird was released after a week in care but subsequently died on the same farm following baiting some months later.

Alphachloralose, a different class of rodenticide from the type described above, was also tentatively identified as being responsible for the poisoning of two Barn Owls received by animal rescue centres – one discovered at a poultry farm, the other at a pig farm. Both birds were taken into care and subsequently recovered.

Slug and snail poisons (metaldehyde) accounted for two separate incidents. Reports were confined to oilseed rape fields in south-eastern England, in situations where large quantities of pellets had been applied. Barn Owl carcases were found close to the fields and were accompanied in two instances by large numbers of small mammal corpses around the treated area.

Secondary poisoning by 'second generation' rodenticides nevertheless appears to pose the greatest poisoning threat to the species today, with most incidents appearing in those areas of the British Isles where rodenticide usage is high and where commensals more commonly constitute a proportion of the Barn Owl's diet.

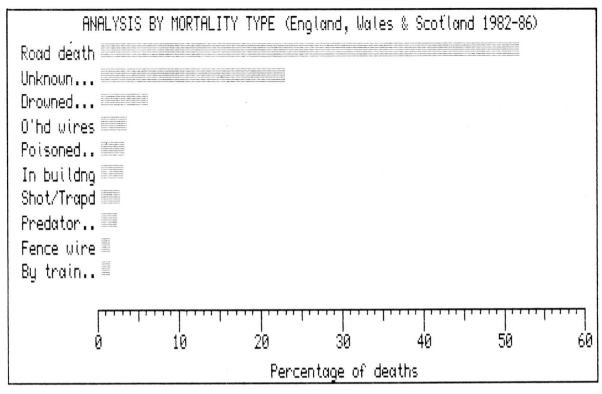

*Fig. 13 **Causes of Barn Owl deaths in England, Wales and Scotland 1982–1986 expressed as a percentage of 746 deaths where cause was known.***

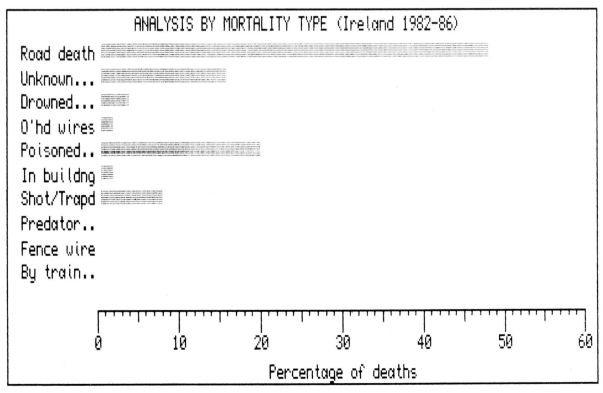

*Fig. 14 **Causes of Barn Owl deaths in Ireland 1982–1986 expressed as a percentage of 50 deaths where cause was known.***

Predation 2.41% (n = 18)

Whilst predation by Tawny Owls has been discussed previously, other predators were reported to have been responsible for mortality. Next to the Tawny Owl, the Goshawk is perhaps the most common avian predator of Barn Owls, and even allowing for its low numbers in Britain (less than 100 pairs), four known incidents were recorded during this *Survey*. In Europe, the Goshawk has previously been identified as a predator of this owl (Mikkola 1976). It is also known that captive Goshawks used in falconry will pursue owls relentlessly and there is therefore little doubt that where these two species overlap in the wild, the Barn Owl is at constant risk of predation.

Other avian species were also responsible for killing Barn Owls. The first incident was believed to have concerned an especially large female Sparrowhawk *Accipiter nisus* in Shropshire, the second a Peregrine *Falco peregrinus* on the Isle of Skye in Scotland and the third a Fulmar *Fulmarus glacialis* on sea cliffs in Yorkshire, death in the latter case arising as a result of being sprayed with Fulmar oil. Although these incidents are of low frequency, they inevitably occur in circumstances where home ranges overlap, and may be more frequent in the case of the Peregrine (and Fulmar) where crag and cliff-nesting Barn Owls commonly occur.

Mink *Mustela vison*, Stoat, Weasel and Brown Rat were also implicated in Barn Owl deaths. In all instances these involved incubating or brooding birds nesting in vulnerable situations, low down in hollow stumps and in fallen trees.

Predation by domestic cats and dogs appears to be very rare in spite of their overlap of home range on farmland. This study substantiates similar remarks made by Bunn *et al* (1982) and the findings of Glue (1971). One unusual incident concerning a dog is nevertheless worth recounting. It occurred in Sussex in 1985 when a Barn Owl attempted to snatch a new born puppy, one of a litter born on a barn floor. This resulted in the bird being bitten by the attendant bitch and although taken into care, the bird died soon after.

Rail Deaths 1.74% (n = 13)

Collision with moving trains has always been a relatively common unnatural cause of mortality to the Barn Owl. Perhaps the earliest record involved a collision with the funnel of a steam locomotive travelling between Kelso and Roxborough in 1876 (Brotherston in Bolam 1912), and not long after this the importance of railside foraging grounds to owls became recognised (Macpherson and Duckworth 1886).

Between 1910 and 1969, Glue found that train victims accounted for 11% of reported mortality. In spite of the increased speed of modern diesel and electric units today, the loss of 7,000 miles of the rail network in the mid-1960s may in part account for the apparent reduction in the numbers of Barn Owls dying from this cause. Alternatively, this decrease may simply reflect a bias in the source from which these data were gathered; however rail employees were well represented in the present *Survey*.

Whatever the reason, train victims today appear as an insignificant cause of mortality by comparison with the large numbers of Barn Owls killed on our modern roads.

Aircraft Deaths 0.54% (n = 4)

Three of these incidents concerned birds found alongside the runway at RAF Valley in Anglesey and one at Blackpool Airport. Numerous other deaths from this cause occurred on the Channel Islands.

Seasonal Mortality

Unlike the situation involving the cause of death, monthly mortality statistics are much less likely to be biased by the source from which the information is derived. The overall pattern of seasonal mortality for the Barn Owl over the period 1982-1986 was therefore compiled from the combined records of the *Survey* itself, the records of taxidermists and from the details of birds submitted for post-mortem investigation (n = 705); data from the last two sources (n = 155) being used to construct the pattern of mortality demonstrated by male and female birds. These monthly distributions are shown in Figures 15, 16 and 17.

Mortality shows a fascinating pattern. The mean laying date for Barn Owls in the British Isles (mainly England) is considered to be the 9th May (Bunn *et al* 1982). From the result of the *Survey* it can be seen that the death rate is lowest in the period leading up to May and throughout the following month of June when most female birds are safely confined to the nest site during the period of incubation and initial brooding.

A noticeable July peak then follows. This is mainly observed in females, coinciding with the time when the nest site is vacated for the first time since egg-laying began. It can be seen that the large proportion of these July deaths are the result of drowning, and as previously discussed, this may be due to the bird's overriding need to remove soiling and parasites after prolonged nest confinement.

The mean fledging date is in mid-August. Thereafter a steep increase in mortality begins in September reaching a peak during October and November at the time when most young birds are attaining independence. Although male mortality appears to lag slightly behind that of females, the pattern shows no major division for the sexes over these months.

By December, overall mortality has fallen, only to rise once again to a large peak during the months of February and March when snowcover is more prolonged and the stress brought on by lack of food is greatest. Unlike the previous October/November peak which Glue (1973) has shown includes approximately 65% juveniles, this new peak in late winter reflects birds of an older age group with juveniles now accounting for only 40% of the total. Whilst no significant differences occur between the sexes at this time, males show some increased mortality trend. This is possibly caused by the stress involved in locating (and defending) good hunting grounds in readiness for breeding.

A breakdown of the major known causes of mortality by month into road deaths, drowning and emaciation is also shown in Figures 18 and 19. With the exception of drowning, which peaks in July, the other causes of death follow a similiar monthly pattern.

Previous studies have indicated that mortality during the first year of a Barn Owl's life is particularly high, ranging from 67% in the Midwest of the USA (Henny 1969), 64-68% in Switzerland (Schifferli 1957; Glutz and

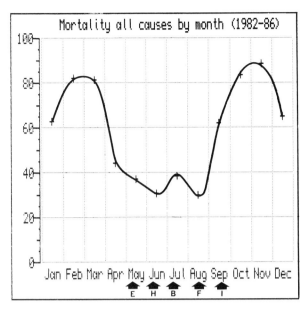

Fig. 15 *Barn Owl mortality in the British Isles 1982–1986 from all causes analysed by month.*

(E – mean egg-laying date, H – hatching, B – continuous brooding ceases, F – mean fledging date, I – young become independent).

Fig. 16 *Monthly analysis of female Barn Owls found dead from all causes in the British Isles expressed as a percentage of 73 known female deaths.*

Fig. 17 *Monthly analysis of male Barn Owls found dead from all causes in the British Isles expressed as a percentage of 82 known male deaths.*

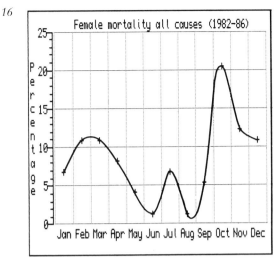

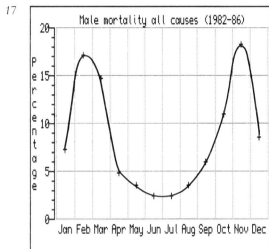

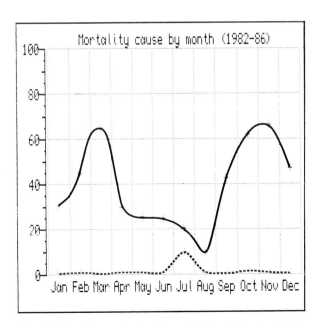

Fig. 18 **Monthly analysis of Barn Owl road deaths (solid line) and deaths by drowning (broken line) in the British Isles 1982–1986.**

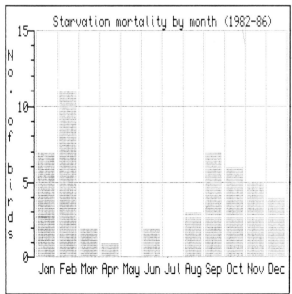

Fig. 19 **Monthly analysis of the number of Barn Owls known to have died of starvation in the British Isles 1982–1986.**

Bauer in Cramp 1985), 73% in East Germany (Schonfeld 1977) to 75% in Denmark and Sweden (Frylestam 1972). In the British Isles it is reported to be about 75% during the first four months following the bird's independence (Lack 1986).

Summarising therefore, it can be seen that two peaks of mortality occur: during late autumn (September – November) and late winter (February–March). The overall pattern is the same as that demonstrated by death due to emaciation alone, indicating that stress caused by hunger is likely to be the reason for peak mortality during these months. Road casualties also demonstrate the same monthly mortality trend, suggesting that roadside hunting may increase in response to seasonal food shortages. The late autumn peak includes predominantly inexperienced but independent juveniles, at a time when the food supply is declining. The late winter peak, involving a greater proportion of adult birds, coincides with the months when snowcover is most prolonged. Male birds may be at greater risk at this time, because of the additional pressures of finding suitable prey-rich breeding grounds in readiness for courtship. Finally, the total annual rates of male and female mortality, sampled from the population over the *Survey* period, are approximately equal (82:73). *For a summary of the findings of the full post-mortem investigations conducted between 1982-1986 see Appendix V.*

PART IV – CONSERVATION

INTRODUCTION: THE SPECIES IN LAW

The general scarcity of the Barn Owl in the 1960s coupled with its apparent long-term decline in numbers, resulted in 1966 in the species' placement on the list of rarities in Part I of the First Schedule of the Protection of Birds Act 1954. There it joined other well known birds of prey which included the Golden Eagle *Aquila chrysaetos*, Red Kite, Merlin *Falco columbarius*, Osprey *Pandion haliaetus* and Snowy Owl *Nyctea scandiaca*. Species in Part I of this schedule (now included in the Wildlife and Countryside Act 1981) are protected in Great Britain by special penalties over and above those attached to the majority of other wild birds. Offences which involve trapping, killing, intentional disturbance at the nest or possession of a wild Barn Owl, its egg or skin can incur a maximum fine of up to £2,000. Under exceptional circumstances, the relevant Nature Conservancy Council licence will be issued to allow research or photography to be undertaken at the nest site.

Wild Barn Owls recovering from injury or which are unfit for return to the wild may be kept in captivity. Aviary-bred Barn Owls can however be kept permanently and may be offered for sale or exchange but only if they are close-ringed (bred in captivity and leg-ringed at the owlet stage, usually around two weeks old, with an unbroken metal ring). Unlike the situation concerning diurnal birds of prey, registration with the Department of the Environment (DOE) is not required for either the bird itself or its owner. Carcases of Barn Owls which have died naturally can be retained or mounted but only sellers registered with the DOE can possess or advertise such specimens for the purpose of sale.

A broadly parallel situation exists in Northern Ireland under the Wildlife (NI) Order 1985 and the Nature Conservation and Amenity Lands (NI) Order 1985, where once again the Barn Owl is subject to special protection and a maximum fine of £2,000.

DETERMINING THE THREAT TO THE BARN OWL ON A REGIONAL BASIS

The Barn Owl's abundance in the British Isles has been shown in each 10-km square. However, in order to determine how seriously threatened this species is within a particular region, it becomes necessary to take into account the population level over a wider area than that of an individual square. For example, whilst a square may consistently hold just one pair of birds and, in isolation, might be considered to have reached critical population levels (ie no longer self-sustaining), it may nevertheless continue to remain viable by virtue of the fact that it is constantly replenished by birds from adjacent districts themselves containing higher densities. However, it is known that there is little movement of Barn Owls out of their natal areas and this highly sedentary behaviour appears to result in only 24% of birds ringed as fledglings dispersing distances greater than 20 km (Lack 1986). In reality, average movement is probably nearer 10 km. Additionally, high levels of mortality occur in first year birds, with 75% of fledged young dying in the first few months of winter (Lack 1986).

This high initial mortality coupled with a limited willingness to disperse over distances greater than 10-20 km means that recolonisation into new or depleted regions is unlikely to occur rapidly.

Taking into account normal dispersal distances of between 10-20 km the Barn Owl may be considered to have reached '*critical*' levels when numbers have declined

73

to 0–2.5 breeding pairs per 100 km² throughout an area of 45 × 45 km (approx 2,000 km²). Using this same criterion, densities of 2.5–4.0 pairs can be classed as '*vulnerable*', (likely to move into the critical category) and more than four pairs, '*stable*' (viable in the foreseeable future).

Since the Vice-counties themselves average approximately 2,000 km² in area, they lend themselves well to expressing the Barn Owl's status in these terms. These three categories have therefore been shown in Table 2 for each Vice-county in England, Wales and Scotland.

CONSERVATION PLAN FOR THE BRITISH ISLES

The decline of the Barn Owl population, which as we have seen has not occurred suddenly but has taken place over the last fifty years, has been the result of detrimental changes in winter weather patterns which, coupled with agricultural improvement, now severely limit the species' food supply. It would seem probable, given the decline in prey abundance, together with the much increased level of unnatural mortality (essentially from road traffic), that the present population in much of the British Isles has simply declined to a level near to the carrying capacity of the available habitat.

Even in situations where it is commonly said that Barn Owls have disappeared from high quality habitats, the reasons for the decline can usually be traced to detrimental changes which have occurred beyond the farm or even the district in question. For example, whilst many individual farms and estates still maintain ideal sheltered habitat they have nevertheless often ended up as fragmented oases in regions of intensively farmed and inhospitable land. As a consequence, small isolated Barn Owl populations, because of their highly sedentary nature, have been unable to remain self-sustaining because the influx of new birds is insufficient to replace those which die.

Long-term conservation of this species can only be achieved effectively by methods which attempt to reinstate the food supply. This can only occur through the maintenance and re-establishment of rough grassland edges in a way which can once again provide continuity from farm to farm and county to county.

For this reason, the two most active conservation initiatives currently being pursued, which involve the blanket provision of nestboxes at new sites and the reintroduction into the wild of captively reared Barn Owls, are unlikely to result in any long-term benefit until the underlying cause has first been corrected.

The conservation theme which now follows has emerged from the overall conclusions of the *Survey*. This theme has been divided here into two main concepts:
1. Protection and enhancement of the Barn Owl strongholds in the British Isles where healthy communities exist and from which expansion could reasonably be expected in the future following improvements in habitat quality and climate.
This can be achieved by the improvement of habitat components, in particular the grassland margins of rivers, ditches, fields, woodland and hedgerows; and the protection and provision of nesting sites within farm buildings and trees.

2. Maintenance and restoration of the complex yet fragile network of Barn Owl corridors on a nation-wide basis.

1. Protection of Barn Owl Strongholds: Conservation on the Farm and Estate

The protection of habitat for the Barn Owl in the British Isles rests today, as indeed it has in the past, with each individual landowner, farmer, forester and gamekeeper. If their enthusiasm for this *Survey* and its conservation initiatives has been an indication of their interest, then there is little reason to doubt their future resolve as far as this species' protection is concerned. It is likely that the success of the countryman of the future will be judged not only by the quantity of food, timber or game he is able to produce but by the diversity and number of wild species, such as the Barn Owl, he can attract to his land.

Top priority must now be given to maintaining and developing existing Barn Owl communities in those areas of the British Isles where the population continues to thrive. This appears to be the best means of halting the overall decline and preparing for expansion in the future.

How can individual landowners, farmers, local countryside groups and other authorities identify those areas within their regions which require priority attention? In general terms, these are to be found on farmland below 100 m adjacent to waterways, wetlands and coastal marshes. It is here where the rough grasslands provide the much needed continuity of habitat permitting the successful dispersal and interaction of young, leading to the maintenance of thriving communities. In national terms, these prime areas can be identified from Map 13 which generally reflects the centres of county populations.

(a) *Improvement of Rough Grassland Edges on Farmland*

This *Survey* has revealed that successful breeding depends upon the extent and quality of grassland edge within the Barn Owl's normal hunting range of 3 km² (300 ha). The length of grassland boundary, be it hedgerow, ditch or woodland, must amount in total to 15–25 km ie. 5–8 km per square kilometre (100 ha). The recommendations being made here for creating and expanding headland widths and providing better quality hedgerows and riversides are consistent with those being made by Game Conservancy scientists for improving habitat for the Grey Partridge *Perdix perdix*. It is hoped that habitat management for the Barn Owl on farmland can in part be achieved in association with conservation plans for lowland gamebirds.

Grassland margins 5–10 m wide can easily be created by permanently expanding the rough edges along existing natural features such as rivers, ditches, hedgerows and woodland edge. In addition, wide headlands can be provided around fields, perhaps selecting first those which are less productive in farming terms. Figure 6 indicates the idealised grassland foraging grounds which provide the model for the creation of these grassland edges. Once created they need little maintenance but can be cut in five year rotation to prevent the invasion of scrub.

Map 13 **Barn Owl strongholds in need of primary protection.**

(b) *Attracting Wild Prey in Winter*

Winter food supply for the Barn Owl has become much depleted as farmland has become more hygienic and annual snowcover more prolonged since the 1940s. Whilst the provision of wide field headlands allows for increased foraging opportunities throughout the year, the maintenance of food during the snow-covered days of winter is of equal importance, requiring further conservation initiatives. As we have seen, it is during these periods of snowcover that the bird is most at risk from a reduction in food, which can subsequently lead to poor breeding success and, in particularly severe winters, increased mortality.

The most practical way of combining the prey advantages of the old rickyard in winter and the grassland foraging edge, is for farmers and game-keepers to provide food dumps (of waste grain and rootcrops) along hedgerow bottoms and around field headlands. Old bales of straw can be used to contain this food in a similar manner to that used by gamekeepers providing pheasant feed. These can be strategically positioned well away from the farm itself (to reduce unwanted pests) along grassland edges which are known to be on the Barn Owl's regular beat. Additionally, waste grain can be placed within isolated buildings (especially where Barn Owls are known to roost) in order to provide a focus of activity for mice, voles and other small rodents.

(c) *Supplementary Feeding in Winter*

Although Barn Owls are reluctant to take carrion (except when the nesting female has large food caches at her disposal), scavenging nevertheless does occur in situations of extreme food shortage. The *Survey* has shown that Barn Owls are known to feed on road casualties and have also resorted to taking meat from a bird table in very severe winters. Indeed, a number of farmers have with some success provided supplementary food, in the form of mice caught in spring traps, at known winter roosts. Artificial feeding with culled day old chicks has also been undertaken at other sites with excellent results. Unfortunately, feeding in this way can meet with practical difficulties since food rapidly chills and eventually freezes under severe winter conditions, making it unacceptable to the birds. Nevertheless, with ingenuity (for example the provision of food late in the evening), artificial feeding can be successful in cases where winter roosting sites have been identified. Food such as freshly killed day old cockerels can usually be obtained from a commercial hatchery at any time during the year and can be stored deep frozen ready for use in the event of a severe winter. The food should be positioned at the Barn Owl roost or preferably the bird's exit from the building, in order to avoid unnecessary disturbance which can involve the owl in wasteful expenditure of energy.

Two food items such as a dead mouse or day old chick can be sufficient supplementary food for one day to enable the Barn Owl to maintain body condition and survive during snowcover or periods of extended frosts. The most severe snow conditions usually occur during the months of February – March but rarely exceed 20 days of continuous cover in most winters. It is therefore only over this relatively short period in the year when artificial feeding should be considered necessary and can be of benefit.

Supplementary feeding at a selected number of vulnerable sites in the wild has consistently resulted in early breeding and double-brooding when sites on adjacent farms failed entirely or produced small broods.

(d) *Conservation and Provision of Nest Sites*

Barn Owls, like birds of prey in general, show a high degree of fidelity to their nesting sites, many of which are used season after season. There is good evidence that some sites go back over the centuries, usually vacated only when the adjoining hunting area has become unsuitable or the nesting site iself has been substantially modified, destroyed or subject to increased human disturbance.

It is however, a common misconception that the blanket provision of new nestboxes within a given region, or the erection of artificial sites in areas where Barn Owls are rare or unknown, will lead to additional occupancy and an increase in the population. As we have previously seen, for example, at least 6,000 of these boxes exist in the British Isles, yet only a small proportion (probably less than 10%) are currently occupied and many of these only because they have been erected at already used nesting or roosting sites. In the majority of situations, it is not the shortage of nest sites but the lack or continuing loss of foraging areas which is the major factor currently limiting the population from recovering or expanding. The widespread provision of boxes in the absence of firm knowledge of the local Barn Owl population, can therefore, be wasteful of resources and effort.

However, the protection of traditional or potentially suitable nest sites within prime habitats where Barn Owls are known to be roosting is of direct importance for this bird's survival.

(i) *Hay Barns*

The *Survey* has shown that hay and straw stacks provide one of the most important breeding sites in the British Isles constituting 39% of all those in agricultural buildings. Whilst bale stacks are among the most secure and secluded of modern agricultural sites when selected by the birds in early spring, they become the most vulnerable soon after egg-laying (in April and May) if bales are steadily removed. This is a particular problem when spring is late and hay is more rapidly consumed owing to the slow growth of grass. Indeed a large majority of the occupied nest sites notified to the *Survey* were only found when stacks were being dismantled. From an analysis of the nest sites used in the British Isles, it can be estimated that about 60% of these sites alone are lost to unintentional human disturbance annually, accounting for the failure of around 450 pairs.

In view of the extreme vulnerability of this important class of breeding site the highest national priority must be given to ensuring the increased safety of these sites in the future.

Therefore when young Barn Owls (or well incubated eggs from which the young can be heard calling) are inadvertently discovered, when dismantling a bale stack, the site should be carefully reconstructed or they should be transferred to a similar site in an undisturbed section of the remaining stack. Failing this, a nestbox complete with ledge can be temporarily erected in the roof space of the same barn or an adjoining building. Brood transfer of this type is usually successful since the food calls of the young are generally sufficient stimulus for the adults to return and for normal feeding to continue the following evening. A tea chest or any other large box which comes to hand can be used for this purpose bearing in mind the operation should be carried out speedily.

The single most effective means of reducing the enormous losses incurred as a result of breeding failure at bale stack sites is to provide more secure and permanent quarters. Whilst a nestbox in the barn roof is essential for future years, the Barn Owls may often continue to select the bales themselves in which to nest. The birds can be encouraged to select a specific part of the stack if a single tunnel is left between bales about two-thirds of the way up the outside face of a bale stack in an open dutch barn, for example, or on the inner face within a more enclosed barn. The tunnel should be 9″–12″ wide and about three bales deep. When constructed in the rear of the stack which is normally the last part to be consumed, this gives the birds an increased opportunity to breed undisturbed. A number of farmers already construct tunnels such as these in a triple stack of bales at the rear of the barn, left for this purpose. This stack is allowed to remain permanently in place for as long as the bales remain serviceable, whilst new bales are annually added to, and consumed from the rest of the barn in the usual manner. Ideally it is preferable to construct two such tunnels in the face of the stack to provide Barn Owls with alternative sites.

If all farmers who were aware of Barn Owls in their area were to provide naturally constructed sites such as these, it would be possible substantially to reduce the high level of breeding failure which commonly occurs in hay and straw barns today and to increase the number of fledged young by about 1,500 per year!

(ii) Other Farm Buildings and Churches

It is often difficult to encourage Barn Owls into newly erected artificial boxes when traditional sites have become unsuitable because of renovation, destruction or advanced decay. However, some success can be achieved by including purpose-built quarters for the birds in newly renovated buildings and churches which have held Barn Owls in the past. The increased human usage which often accompanies renovation will however often preclude occupancy and entrances to such sites should be positioned on the most secluded side of the building.

Careful inspection of other old buildings within those areas where nest sites have recently been lost can often indicate alternative roosting sites from the copious amounts of 'whitewash' on beams and black pellets on the floor. It is at the least disturbed of these that nestboxes should be placed, preferably in advance of any anticipated disruption of the original site. Alternatively, boxes can be erected in nearby hay barns or some other suitable structure.

There is also some evidence from a Hawk Trust project that nestboxes placed at traditional (but vulnerable) nesting sites in old buildings are often accepted by the birds in preference to a natural ledge or cavity nest site, with a marginal improvement in breeding success. Boxes should only be erected however, where failure occurs at the natural site because it is exposed to weather or in situations where the young regularly fall from the nest. Boxes should not be erected at natural sites where they are likely to attract any additional unwanted human attention. Boxes should be erected between October and February to avoid the possibility of any disturbance to the birds which may already be occupying the site during the breeding period. Many sites in derelict farm buildings can be preserved by carrying out simple repairs to the roof.

(iii) Nestboxes in Trees

Approximately 30% of Barn Owls in Britain nest in the cavities of isolated hedgerow and parkland trees, but in the wetter districts this is a rare breeding site. Protection of trees assumes a high priority in regions where they are the predominant class of nest site. The Town and Country Planning Act 1971, Section 60 contains provision for Tree Preservation Orders (TPOs) designed to prevent wilful damage or felling of valued trees in town and country. Normally, the criteria used to judge the importance of a tree are its quality, age, natural beauty and amenity value. To date, there have been no test cases to confirm whether or not a TPO can be placed by virtue of the fauna and flora the tree might contain. The presence of an endangered species may nevertheless be considered to constitute part of its natural beauty or amenity value and be interpreted as such by the local authority when considering a TPO. For maximum success however, tree preservation orders should be sought from the District Council Tree Officer primarily on the value of the tree itself. TPOs can usually be justified for most mature trees (except those which are dead or dangerous).

Old hollow tree stumps containing nesting places which have become exposed can be capped to extend the lifespan of the site. Specially designed tree nestboxes can also be erected to replace natural cavities within trees which have fallen or been felled. Sometimes, these can be fixed within the hollow stump itself.

Caution should however be exercised when considering the siting of tree nestboxes since their large size can draw unwanted human attention particularly in areas to which the public has free access. Erection of tree boxes in the high rainfall regions of western Britain where Barn Owls rarely use natural tree sites, can be wasteful of effort and indeed counter-productive by encouraging Tawny

8. The hedge-lined boundaries of small fields in lowland river valleys provide the ideal hunting habitat. (J. Orchel)

9. The banks of drainage ditches provide vole-rich grassland corridors in regions of intensively farmed land in Lincolnshire.

10. The re-establishment of rough grassland margins along riversides and fields is one of the most important conservation measures.

11. An old farmstead in southern England. Hay bales provide the most commonly used nesting site in farm buildings.

TABLE 13

Anticoagulant Rodenticides Currently Marketed in the UK

'Second generation' anticoagulants
(To be avoided on farms where Barn Owls are known to be present)

Chemical name	Trade Names and Marketing Companies
Brodifacoum	Brodifacoum Bait (Sorex Co Ltd); Klerat, Ratak Plus (ICI).
Bromadiolone	Bromard, Bromatrol, Bromex, Deadline (Rentokil Ltd); Slaymore (Ceiba Geigy Agrochem).
Difenacoum	Neosorexa (Sorex Co Ltd); Fentrex (Rentokil Ltd); Ratak (ICI); Ratrick (Farm Protection Ltd).

'First Generation' anticoagulants
(The rodenticides of choice in areas where rats demonstrate little resistance to these chemicals.)

Chemical name	Trade Names and Marketing Companies
Warfarin	Rinoxin, Detrimor (Gerthardt Pharm Ltd); Grovex (W H Groves and Family Ltd); Klearwell Warfarin (Layson Ltd); Biotrol (Rentokil Ltd); Sorexa, Sorex Plus (Sorex Co Ltd); Scram (E C De Witt Co Ltd); Sakarat (Killgerm Chem Ltd); Rodentex Universal (Rodentex Ltd); Len-Ro-Di (Ovelle Ltd); Kilmol (Callisto Aviaries Ltd); Action Rat Mouse Exterminator (Crown Chem Co Ltd); Arrest a Pest (Pet & Pest Products Ltd).
Diphacinone	Diphacin (Velsicol Chem Corp).
Chlorophacinone	Drat (May & Baker Ltd); Karate (Dexter Chem Ltd); Klearwell Drat (Layson Ltd); Ridento (Farmers Lab Ltd).
Coumatetralyl	Racumin (Bayer UK Ltd/Pan Britannica Ind); Townex (Town & Country Pest Services).

Source: (Pesticides Safety Precautions Scheme – booket 1984)

Owls (see 'Other Conservation Issues' below).

(e) *Avoiding Disturbance*
Barn Owls are extremely sensitive to human disturbance, especially at newly occupied sites and particularly during the early stages of breeding from April to the end of June. Desertion of nests can result following close inspection or increased disturbance around the nest site during these early stages. Landowners and farmers should also be aware that the ringing of young Barn Owls and the close inspection of nests even by qualified and licensed researchers cannot always guarantee the safety of their Barn Owls. For this reason, permission to check nest contents or to ring Barn Owls should only be considered by the landowner if the aims of the research being conducted outweigh the slight but nevertheless potential risk of nest failure. This caution has been issued to Barn Owl researchers in the past by those well qualified to judge (Bunn *et al* 1982) but still ringers are actively encouraged to increase their efforts every year in the name of research and conservation. All too often the welfare of the Barn Owl takes second place to the number of 'entries' on a ringing card.

(f) *Preventing Drowning*
Drowning in water tanks was found to be the most significant cause of mortality on farmland. Often this occurred year after year on some farms within close proximity to the nest site. Drowning can be avoided quite simply by floating a close-fitting plank of wood in the trough or tank. This continues to allow livestock to drink but prevents owls from submerging.

2. Maintenance and Restoration of Grassland Corridors
Figure 6 indicates the grassland habitat types most commonly favoured by Barn Owls for hunting. They all possess similar properties. They are largely unmanaged or lightly grazed damp grasslands which are often banked or ditched. Many are skirted by boundary posts or stands of hedgerow, providing the birds with additional opportunities for perching or 'still hunting'. These habitats are all of a linear nature or have linear features within them such as river, ditch, bank, hedgerow or woodland edge.

Attempts must be made to restore, enhance and develop a nationwide network of linear grasslands such as these on farmland throughout the British Isles. Prime attention should be given to the waterway networks by allowing natural regeneration of open grassland at least 10 m wide to develop along the banks of lowland waterway systems.

(a) *'Riverside Link' (A Hawk Trust Scheme)*
The local Water Authorities and Internal Drainage Boards are in the best positions to establish, through sympathetic management, this nationwide network of grassland riverside corridors. In Lincolnshire, the Anglian Water Authority has already introduced conservation measures for the species with commitment and enthusiasm following a regional riverside corridor plan drawn up and supervised by the author. As other authorities follow suit, opportunities will develop for providing countrywide continuity of rough grasslands for this species in Britain.

(b) *'Farmland Link' (A Hawk Trust Scheme)*
In addition to the 'Riverside Link' scheme, landowners and farmers can pool interests to produce a similar network of linked grasslands farm to farm using streamsides, field headlands, ditches and small woodlands, the details of which are described in more detail above. A pilot scheme in Buckinghamshire known as 'Farmland Link' is presently underway involving five large farms and estates following a plan prepared and supervised by the author. The current provision of Government grants for farm woodlands for example can assist in the development of these boundary networks.

OTHER CONSERVATION ISSUES

Use of Rodenticides
Rodent infestations on farms, although much less serious than fifty years ago, can remain a potential problem from the point of view of damage to stored foods and the risk to human health. Today, rat and mouse control is most commonly undertaken by professional operators employed by companies specialising in pest control. Except in situations where dogs, cats and livestock have suffered accidental poisoning from rodenticides, farmers, not unnaturally, show little interest in identifying which type of chemical is being applied around their farms.

Survey reports indicate that the majority of farmers consider regular rodenticide application unnecessary in situations where Barn Owls are present. However, there are times when chemical control is required and it then becomes of major importance to ensure that the chemicals which are used are those which are least dangerous to owls and indeed other wild and domestic animals.

The most toxic modern rodenticides are collectively known as the 'second generation' anticoagulants and these chemicals together with their trade names are listed at the beginning of Table 13. These poisons must be avoided if the risk of secondary poisoning is to be minimised. In most situations, excellent alternatives are available.

It is important that these potent 'second generation' anticoagulants are not confused with warfarin which together with the rodenticides in the second half of this Table, although chemically similar, demonstrate a markedly lower toxicity. As a result these are potentially less dangerous to owls.

Data Requirements for Approval Under the Control of Pesticides Regulations 1986 (MAFF 1986) calls for an assessment by the manufacturers of the non-target hazard of these compounds. Particular attention should be paid to those species of birds considered most at risk. Endangered species must be given priority. Guidelines for experimental field trials suggest census counts of wild birds before and after application of the pesticide (by observers walking a fixed route around the site) followed by a systematic search for casualties. However, this clearly would be inadequate for an elusive and nocturnal species and one which in the author's experience often dies out of sight at a secluded roost in a tree cavity or barn roof.

The 'second generation' anticoagulants fall into the highest category of pesticide toxicity ('very toxic') and the urgency for controlling rodent infestations not infrequently result in the misuse of these poisons especially in the field situation. The secondary poisoning hazard of these compounds to Barn Owls is now undeniable. Limitation of their use to professional operators in indoor situations, where Barn Owls do not have access, is of major priority and as suggested by the above regulations, product labelling must clearly identify the danger to wild birds.

Captive Breeding and Release

Reintroduction of Barn Owls into the wild although not unlawful, remains a controversial issue in Britain. Concerns relate to the potential loss of wild Barn Owls when reintroduced birds are inadvertently placed in established territories. In practice, however, it is generally the released pair which is lost. Other anxieties relate to the risk of introducing disease into the existing wild population, although post-mortem examinations conducted on captive birds in recent years give no cause for concern at this time. The major argument centres on the stage at which human intervention through reintroduction should take place. For other endangered species, this has previously only begun when the population has already reached critical levels or the species has become extinct. At this stage it is often too late to expect recolonisation from released captive-reared stock to occur rapidly, if at all, especially with species which are sedentary in character.

When assessing the value of any reintroduction scheme it becomes very important to try and establish the root cause of the species' decline in the wild. If the major factor, or factors, can be identified and partially remedied, then subsequent reintroduction becomes a more rational choice. However, (in the past) when other species have diminished to very low levels, remnant communities have shown a potential to recolonise rapidly into depleted areas once the hostile factors are reduced. This has been well demonstrated with the Peregrine, following the reduction in the usage of harmful agricultural chemicals. This emphasises the importance of protecting and enhancing existing wild Barn Owl communities before other conservation measures of this type are considered.

How should the reintroduction of Barn Owls in the British Isles be viewed today? This conservation practice is not new. Noble (1906) reports that 'More than twenty years ago we placed three young birds in an old dovecote at Park Palace and confined them for three weeks, during which time they were fed on mice. On being liberated one left or was driven away, but the others or their descendents have bred annually (with the exception of one year)'.

More recently the practice of Barn Owl reintroduction has been revived (Ratcliffe 1979; Bunn et al 1982; Warburton 1984). Methods are varied but usually involve captive breeding from permanently disabled but otherwise healthy adults. The offspring either as fledglings or adults are then released from a suitably modified farm building within prime habitat during the spring, at a time when small mammal numbers are increasing.

Today, *Survey* results would indicate that about 1,500-2,000 Barn Owls are released into the wild by about 400 operators annually. The number of Barn Owls in captivity probably comes close in number to those existing in the wild, mainly because of the high numbers of Barn Owls injured and rehabilitated and their subsequent high breeding potential. Their enormous capacity to breed and raise large and often multiple broods when food is unlimited, highlights an important aspect of the Barn Owl's breeding biology which is unmatched by any other British bird of prey. On average, a captive pair will rear four young from a brood. Not uncommonly, two or even three broods may be produced. In 1984, for example, sixteen young were reared by one pair from a single clutch of twenty-four fertile eggs. The large numbers of birds produced, result not unnaturally in a keen desire on the part of the owners to see their offspring released into the wild in an attempt to supplement the dwindling wild population.

The inescapable difficulty of Barn Owl reintroduction as a conservation initiative is that even in the most capable hands, the degree of mortality during the bird's first year of life appears to be similar to that experienced in the wild which has been reported at about 75% (Lack 1986). In simple terms, this means that for every pair released, there is a strong possibility that the partnership would not survive intact to breed in the following year.

Monitored studies of a large scale reintroduction programme in Buckinghamshire supported by The Hawk Trust, indicate that of twenty-two pairs released over a period of three years, only three pairs have attempted to breed the following year at their release sites. Although the project is in its early stages, preliminary findings would suggest the release of at least five pairs a year on farms within a confined area would be necessary to retain one breeding pair in the area the following year. Thereafter, in the absence of any immigration of wild birds, similar levels of reintroduction would be needed annually to maintain this level. Warburton for example, has reported that over a period of nine years an average of approximately 4.5 pairs have been released annually producing a minimum of thirty-six fledged young (4 per year) although this was assisted here by the natural pairing of wild and reintroduced Barn Owls on some occasions (Warburton 1984).

The problem of introducing large numbers of birds before any noticeable expansion can be perceived, is compounded by the fact that a large proportion of release programmes are taking place in areas where wild Barn Owl populations have already reached critical levels. In such areas the population has reached this state of decline because the environmental factors operating against the bird are excessively high. Once again, this occurs where land exceeds 100 m, farming methods are intensive or where the density of road traffic is acute. The reintroduction of Barn Owls and the blanket provision of nestboxes in unsuitable habitats is unlikely to result in long-term success.

The reintroduction of Barn Owls nevertheless has a role to play in the conservation of this species; for to condemn or criticise in the absence of knowledge is as negative as sitting back and doing nothing. The conservation benefit must however be viewed more realistically and critically than in the past and the following points provide an indication of what might reasonably be achieved:

a) establishing and maintaining by annual reintroduction, the integrity of a naturalised breeding population to provide people with the opportunity of continuing to observe and enjoy Barn Owls in the wild (as opposed to captivity).

b) a holding exercise to maintain a local population at a viable level to allow expansion to occur naturally once the hostile environmental factors operating against the species have become minimised.

c) allowing greater knowledge to be gained about the best methods of reintroduction should it become imperative in the future.

d) providing a means of studying an essentially free-living Barn Owl population without threatening existing wild and often fragile communities.

Barn Owl reintroduction should therefore only be considered by teams with considerable expertise. Operators should always maintain a full written account of the work, and the BTO should actively encourage the ringing of all these birds to provide information about the effectiveness of reintroduction programmes. Reintroduction should not normally be contemplated in regions where the land exceeds 100 m and where winter snowcover can exert very heavy losses. Nor should it be considered in areas of intensive cultivation or where traffic density within a 3 km radius is high. A minimum of five unrelated pairs (or an equivalent number of young birds) should be released on farms within a small area, preferably close to river networks or wetlands to provide for future interchange between offspring and to maintain genetic diversity and vigour.

Single pairs released at scattered locations have little chance of any long-term success. The introduction of single birds during April or May at sites where wild owls are known to be unpaired may however prove to be one of the most worthwhile conservation measures for maintaining local populations. *Reintroduction is not a method to be recommended to landowners or farmers in circumstances where the release of a single isolated pair is contemplated and for this reason, details of the methods of reintroduction are not given here.*

Competition for Tree Nestboxes between Barn Owls and Tawny Owls

As previously shown, it has been strongly suspected, but not proven that the decline of the Barn Owl in Britain may be due in part to the rapid increase in the Tawny Owl population over the last fifty years. It has been shown that tree-nesting Tawny Owls will kill Barn Owls competing for nest sites (by interspecific aggression) Mikkola (1976), and because the former selects its site early in the year this bird may by its presence alone prevent Barn Owls nesting in these tree cavities by competitive exclusion. Observations by the author suggest that the predation of Barn Owls by Tawny Owls commences in some areas as soon as ideal nesting opportunities are presented to the latter.

The Tawny Owl readily accepts nestboxes sited in trees, even when they have been specifically designed for Barn Owls and often in preference to natural tree cavities. Because of its more resourceful nature, this owl can often be tempted to redistribute and expand its population out of deep woodland habitat into more open countryside following the provision of large numbers of artificial breeding sites. Indeed, Tawny Owls often abandon natural sites when presented with nestboxes placed in high density in certain habitats (Ratcliffe and Petty 1986).

Today almost every small piece of woodland, copse and municipal park contains at least one pair of Tawny Owls. There is, in habitat terms therefore, often a restricted and hence fragile separation between these two species. In many regions this separation is probably only ensured by the Tawny Owl's reluctance to nest within buildings.

Mikkola, when discussing the conservation of owls writes, 'clearly the existence of interspecific aggression makes it pointless to attract 'weaker' owl species into territories of 'stronger' species' or vice versa. There is therefore a danger that by encouraging an even closer competition between these two owls by the provision of artificial nesting sites for Tawny Owls, Barn Owls themselves will become displaced. For example, an increasing trend over the last twenty years has been to provide large numbers of Tawny Owl nestboxes, often to assist research studies. When erected outside woodland, these have the potential slowly to reduce local Barn Owl numbers, or to inhibit their recovery. Likewise, the provision of Barn Owl tree nestboxes in the wetter regions of Britain, where the existing population exclusively selects buildings in which to nest, is likely to result in encouraging Tawny Owls, perhaps leading to the displacement of Barn Owls from long-used sites nearby.

Today, for example, a number of nestbox projects commendably seek to increase Barn Owl numbers within commercial forestry in northern Britain by providing large numbers of regularly spaced artificial nesting sites on coniferous trees around the woodland edge. The Barn Owl nests primarily in old buildings in these regions and serious attempts should be made to conserve these sites. The provision of new tree sites may actually have a far greater potential to allow the Tawny Owl its first opportunity to redistribute and expand into areas rich in prey and where the lack of secure nesting sites in old tree cavities was previously limiting.

Should the expansion of this hardier and more adaptable species occur as a result, then this may in fact serve to reduce the existing but fragile Barn Owl population in the region, restricting access to its prime foraging areas around the forest edge as a consequence of aggressive competition from the Tawny Owl. Any scheme which has the potential to expand the Tawny Owl population in Britain outside woodland should be viewed with great caution.

FUTURE RECOMMENDATIONS

Long-term Monitoring of Population Levels

Having established a population figure for the British Isles for the mid-1980s, future monitoring of the Barn Owl in Britain and Ireland remains necessary as an early warning system against continued decline, as well as a means of evaluating the effectiveness of the conservation measures being undertaken.

The Hawk Trust is to undertake a full four year follow-up survey beginning in 1992, and already the planning phases of this project are underway.

A National Conservation Programme for the Barn Owl

A 'Barn Owl Observer Network' is to be expanded throughout the British Isles. This will assist with future population monitoring, conservation implementation, and the expansion of the national 'Farmland and Riverside Links Schemes' which seek to provide a nationwide network of rough grassland habitat corridors. It is anticipated that these link schemes will be conducted in conjunction with the CLA, Game Conservancy, NFU and Water Authorities. It is hoped that a grant system to farmers will be devised in conjunction with the Nature Conservancy Council, to encourage the creation of these grassland corridors. It is initially intended that these will radiate from the centres of Barn Owl population on lowland farms in England and Wales.

Research and Conservation

A number of priority research projects have been devised based on the findings of this report. They will include habitat studies in a number of differing natural and farming environments, rodenticide research and other projects intended to provide more detailed information about the species' requirements on modern farmland. This information will be augmented in due course by the findings of the computer simulations of Barn Owl ecology which are now being developed.

Educational materials for schools and the farming community are being prepared on the basis of this report to supplement the proposed 'Barn Owl Observer Network' scheme.

APPENDIX I

WORLD DISTRIBUTION

The Barn Owl *Tyto alba* (Scopoli) is considered to be the most widely distributed land bird in the world, being present in every continent with the exception of Antarctica.

The species is currently believed to be represented by thirty-five different races (Bunn *et al* 1982) extending throughout most of Europe, western Russia, Africa, Pakistan, India, south-eastern Asia, and Australia, through the Pacific Islands to North and South America. It is therefore to be found in widely differing zones ranging from tropical rain forest to desert climates (Voous 1960). The Barn Owl is however absent as a breeding species from most of Scandinavia, northern Russia, Siberia, China, Korea, Japan and from all but the extreme south of Canada. In the Southern Hemisphere it is absent from Antarctica and New Zealand. The northern limit of the Barn Owl's world breeding range currently lies at latitude 58° in the north of Scotland (Shawyer unpublished) and even in the Southern Hemisphere, the species does not extend this far from the equator.

In the British Isles, our own white-breasted race *Tyto alba alba* is the typical sub-species (nominate). This race is predominantly a Mediterranean form found in western Yugoslavia, Greece, Italy, Bulgaria and the islands of Crete and Malta. Its range extends westwards from Asia Minor and Iraq to Egypt, Sicily, the Balearic Isles, Algeria, Morocco through to Tenerife and Gran Canaria to Spain and Portugal. *Tyto a. alba* is also the predominant race in Italy, southern Switzerland, southern and western France, the Channel Islands, Belgium and the British Isles.

The dark-breasted race, *T. a. guttata*, which is sometimes found as a continental straggler to Britain, takes over as the predominant race in eastern France, Germany, Holland, Denmark and Sweden, eastwards to Poland and western Russia and southwards to Austria, Hungary and the Crimea. This race however, overlaps with that of *T.a.a.* in eastern France, Belgium and western Germany and the two interbreed in these regions.

A third European race *T. a. ernesti* also occurs and is confined to Corsica and Sardinia.

Holarctic Status

In spite of the Barn Owl's wide-ranging distribution, there are few countries in the Northern Hemisphere where the species can be described as common. Long-term population declines are being reported in the northern regions of the United States of America and in much of Europe where the mean January isotherm is below 4° C.

America

Because of the threatened status of the Barn Owl *T. a. pratincola* in the United States of America, particularly in the North and Mid-west between latitudes 38° and 47°, the bird is listed on the National Audubon Society's Blue List as a potentially threatened species – one 'which for any number of reasons, known or unknown, appear to be suffering in all, or part of, their range from non-cyclical decline...' (Arib 1979). The situation appears to be quite the reverse however in the Pacific and Atlantic States of the South where there has been little evidence of any significant decrease in numbers and where the species is well established.

The Barn Owl was believed to have extended its range into the Mid-west early in the twentieth century (Colvin *et al* 1984). Today, however, in the more northerly states of the Mid-west such as **Minnesota** the Barn Owl, although not yet listed as endangered appears to be declining (Green and Janssen in Petersen 1980). In **Wisconsin** although the Barn Owl was never common, it was once found breeding more commonly throughout the southern and south-eastern regions of the state. A change in the frequency of sightings since 1950 suggests a declining population and the species is now seriously endangered (Petersen 1980). Throughout **Michigan**, only four verified sightings were reported in 1985 and the species is once again listed as endangered here (Smith 1986). In **Nebraska** where the species was once common it is now a rare breeding bird especially in the North and East, although faring better in the central-southern and western regions (Dinan and Wingfield 1985). It is nevertheless now listed as endangered in the state (Smith 1986). In **Iowa** where the Barn Owl was once again previously common the species is now rare and endangered (Newhouse and Ehresman 1983) with only twelve verified sightings for the state in 1985 (Smith 1986).

In the more southerly states of the Mid-west, the same pattern of decline is emerging. In **Illinois** and **Indiana** for example, where the species was once plentiful, it is now endangered in both states (Smith 1986). In **Ohio** too, although the Barn Owl was well established and common by the 1930s, it has, since 1964, become quite rare (Dexter in Petersen 1980), with only 2 – 10 pairs documented annually between 1980 and 1982 (Colvin *et al* 1984). It is now listed as a potentially threatened species (Tate 1981, Colvin *et al* 1984). Even in the most southerly mid-western state of **Missouri** it is considered one of the most endangered birds of prey, although it was the only state to record an increase over the last three to ten years (Smith 1986).

In summary, therefore, the species is rare in the Mid-west states north of latitude 38° and in North America generally where the mean January isotherm is below 4° C. Increased winter severity can be demonstrated for this region since 1950 – perhaps like the situation in the British Isles, climate has been the major factor responsible for the declining population.

Europe

Throughout most of central and western Europe, particularly in those countries north of latitude 48° where the mean January isotherm is below 4° C and snowcover is far more prolonged, a long-term population decline has been very much apparent over the last few decades. There is some evidence that the Barn Owl first colonised some of these more northerly regions between 1800 and 1850 taking advantage of the warming of the climate (Braaksma 1980; Ziesemer 1980). In these countries today however, the Barn Owl can now be considered uncommon or rare.

A comparable situation exists in the British Isles where January temperatures in the eastern half of the country are below 4° C and snowcover is much more sustained. Here, in contrast to the warmer snow-free southern and western regions, Barn Owl numbers have declined considerably since the worsening of the winter climate in the 1940s.

A brief description of the Barn Owl's status in Europe is now given. Countries are listed in order of decreasing winter severity in terms of mean January temperature and duration of snowcover.

Sweden (*T. a. guttata*)

In the southern province of Scane, where the species is close to the limit of its northern range (lat 56° N), the Barn Owl is now the rarest breeding bird, having declined from a maximum of fifty pairs in the 1870s. A rapid decline followed in the 1950s and 1960s. About five pairs were present in the early 1970s and by 1983 only a single pair remained (Hirschfeld pers.comm.).

Poland (*T. a. guttata*)

In Poland the species has now become localised and generally scarce (Szwagrzak pers.comm.).

Czechoslavakia (*T. a. guttata*)

The Czechoslavak population has shown a marked decline since 1960 (Pikula *et al* 1984; Cramp 1985).

Hungary (*T. a. guttata*)

In Hungary the species is now considered uncommon and to have markedly declined in recent years (Kallay pers.comm.).

Romania (*T. a. guttata*)

The Barn Owl here is a scarce breeding bird but from the limited data that exists it is believed to be more common in the north and west of the country (Munteanu in Mikkola 1983).

Denmark (*T. a. guttata*)

The Danish population was considered to be as low as 75-100 pairs by 1976 (Cramp 1985).

West Germany (*T. a. guttata*)

The West German Bird Atlas considered the species to be threatened nationally (Braaksma 1980). In regions of the North, such as Schleswig Holstein, a serious decline has been reported over the last few decades and following a brief respite during the Second World War, is now considered one of the most threatened species in the region (Ziesemer 1980).

Netherlands (*T. a. guttata*)

A rapid decline has been observed in the Netherlands. Until 1962, 3,000 pairs were estimated to be breeding annually (Honer 1963). Following the severe winter of 1962/63, only eighteen successful pairs were identified. In spite of a slow recovery to 300-700 pairs between 1975 and 1977 (Braaskma and de Bruijn 1976) a setback occurred following the bad winter of 1978/79 such that

latest estimates are less than 100 pairs (de Jong 1985).

Belgium (*T. a. guttata*)

In Belgium the species was noted to have declined by the early 1970s, and quite dramatically in the western and north-eastern districts (Braaksma 1980). The population is currently believed to be about 1,000 pairs (Cramp 1985).

Luxembourg (*T. a. guttata*)

Although the species is well distributed throughout Luxembourg, especially in the South, it remains an endangered species. The population is subject to rapid decline, particularly in the North due to severe winters and especially during periods of prolonged snow. The latest population estimate is 1600 pairs in the Grand Duchy of Luxembourg (Lippens and Wille 1972).

France (*T. a. alba* and *T. a. guttata*)

The French Barn Owl population is unmistakably declining although not as severely as in many other European countries (Yeatman in Braaksma 1980) with an estimated total population in the range of 20,000 – 60,000 pairs (Mikkola 1983).

Bulgaria (*T. a. alba* and *T. a. guttata*)

The Barn Owl is very rare in Bulgaria although both sub-species breed. Little is known however about past population levels to enable any estimate of population changes to be made (Simeonov 1981).

Spain (*T. a. alba*)

A regional decline in Barn Owl numbers began between 1950-1960 in the northern regions of the country. This was believed to be the result of heavy rodenticide applications and not climatic change. Current estimates suggest an overall decrease from 50,000 pairs in 1965, to not less than 30,000 pairs in 1975. The species is not considered threatened although more recent reports suggest a localised decline in the South (Noval pers.comm; Herrera in Bunn *et al* 1982).

Portugal (*T. a. alba*)

Despite a patchy distribution, the Barn Owl is considered common in Portugal (Newton and Chancellor 1985).

Italy (*T. a. alba*)

There has been no evidence of any overall decline in numbers in Italy. Indications of some decrease are of a regional nature and confined to areas of central Italy, where populations have been more extensively studied. Population densities vary from a minimum one pair per 20 km^2 (Contoli pers. comm), to one pair per 130 km^2 in parts of central and western Italy (Lovari *et al* 1976). The Barn Owl is not on the list of rare, declining, endangered or vanishing species.

Since the Barn Owl is primarily considered a species of tropical and Mediterranean type climates, it is perhaps not surprising that any decline, through whatever cause, will be most pronounced as it approaches those less favourable climates towards the limits of its world range.

APPENDIX II

BARN OWL SURVEY OF BRITAIN AND IRELAND – METHODS

Background to the Project

Improved methods of communication together with a skilled national network of amateur ornithologists means that it has now become possible to locate and thereby accurately census the breeding populations of many of our less common bird species. This is especially true for the endangered (Schedule I) birds of prey in Britain because their individual numbers are generally less than 1,000 pairs and are therefore considered relatively small (Newton 1984). In addition this group of birds is also more easily located than many other species since they are commonly restricted to well defined regions of Britain, and because of their specialist habitat requirements often remain closely tied year after year to traditional breeding sites, where occupancy can usually be confirmed from their aerial displays and vocal behaviour during the breeding period. For these reasons the majority of raptors have been censused in recent years with the confidence that few breeding pairs were overlooked.

With the exception of Ireland, where observers are far less numerous than elsewhere, censusing of these diurnal birds of prey can therefore be successfully conducted on a nationwide basis by a limited number of experienced and suitably licensed fieldworkers.

The Barn Owl, on the other hand, is an especially difficult species to census because of its widespread distribution throughout the British Isles, high breeding numbers and elusive nocturnal nature. Indeed, it has previously been considered to be the third most difficult bird to survey (Sharrock 1976). Efficient censusing of this species using classical methods would, therefore, entail large teams of licensed and experienced field workers attempting to cover thoroughly every ten kilometre square in the British Isles. Additionally, even with the most expert and sophisticated coverage, the Barn Owl is commonly overlooked, especially by ornithologists, even on familiar ground. This was demonstrated repeatedly throughout the present *Survey* and has previously been reported by Mead (1982) when he instances a nest site just 800 m from the BTO headquarters at Tring during the 'Atlas' period discovered only when the young were six weeks old!

As well as these practical difficulties, breeding surveys involving the Barn Owl could justifiably be challenged on ethical grounds because of the bird's particular vulnerability to human interference. Indeed the use of intensive research methods are commonly of considerable concern to landowners and farmers, many of whom hold a commendably protective attitude towards this species from any outside disturbance.

In spite of the numerous methodological difficulties, there was however, little doubt several years ago that a full survey of this species was urgently required, since whilst most other birds of prey had increased their numbers in recent years, the Barn Owl was demonstrat-ing a continued decline which appeared to be accelerating.

The Barn Owl Survey of Britain and Ireland was thus initiated following consultation with the BTO in June 1982, in the knowledge that there were no specific plans for a survey of this species in the immediate future. It was therefore intended that the Barn Owl Survey would complement and support the five year surveying programme envisaged by the BTO, which was to involve a number of other priority species (Swann – Report to Scientific Committee of The Hawk Trust, August 1983).

Scope and Objectives

The Survey set out to determine as precisely as possible:

1. The abundance of the Barn Owl in each of 3,862 ten kilometre squares of the British National and Irish Grids.
2. The extent of the long-term population change which had occurred in England and Wales since 1932.
3. The significance of each of the many factors which might be influencing the species' apparent decline.
4. And to provide a sound baseline on which population trends could be assessed in the future.

On the basis of the findings, the overall objective was to initiate a well-structured conservation programme which could actively involve farmers, foresters, game-keepers and landowners, together with other relevant conservation and countryside bodies (backed if necessary by additional legislation).

Project Support

The Barn Owl Survey of Britain and Ireland was jointly funded by The Hawk Trust, The Country Landowners' Association and The World Wildlife Fund through commercial sponsorship from the Office Cleaning Services Group. The author would once again like to express his gratitude to these organisations.

Methodology

Pilot Survey 1982

A pilot survey began following the breeding season of 1982, to determine the most effective methods of obtaining reliable data about the species and the level of information which could be anticipated. It soon became clear that the enquiry was being taken up with considerable enthusiasm and that the data emerging from non-ornithological sources were far more reliable and of much greater detail than was originally anticipated. However, it served to demonstrate the inadequacy of the preliminary questionnaire which placed too great an emphasis on subjective opinion. It also indicated that whilst the questionnaire and recording card formats were providing a high level of response from ornithologists; countrymen including landowners, farmers and keepers preferred to write a detailed longhand account about the Barn Owls with which they were familiar rather than complete this formalised type of questionnaire. In the light of these experiences the subsequent protocol for the full *Survey* was devised.

Map 14 *Survey sample areas.*

Shaded areas show the counties where a major effort was made over the Survey period to census population levels. Solid squares represent those localities where intensive field studies were undertaken.

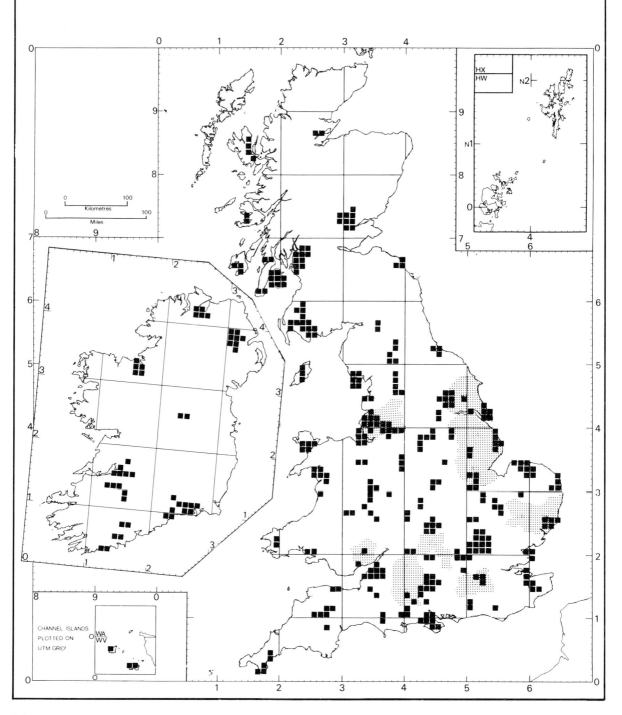

The Full Survey

It also became clear during the pilot survey, that because of the Barn Owl's secretive nature, breeding could rarely be confirmed other than by those who had an intimate and almost daily knowledge of the land in question. One, or even a number of nocturnal visits by observers to a 10-km square rarely provided any sound indication of the number of breeding pairs present, except in those situations where a local specialist had made a detailed study over a period of years. This is well illustrated from one particular square which contained one of the highest Barn Owl densities in Britain, comprising twenty-five breeding pairs. As it transpired, local ornithologists had no knowledge of Barn Owls on this estate, neither had the county bird society received any breeding records either prior to, or during the *Survey* period. This was by no means a local exception. The following is not intended as any criticism; however, the number of breeding Barn Owls notified to county recorders on average underestimated the true county population by about 85% (except in those circumstances where special county surveys had been commissioned).

For the full *Survey* to succeed it clearly needed a novel approach, distinct from the methods previously used for censusing other bird species. Not only was it imperative to obtain reliable data, but at the same time the enquiry needed to guarantee absolute confidentiality of notified breeding sites to protect not only the birds themselves but the wishes of the observers and landowners.

The *Survey* set out to achieve wide and intensive media coverage based on the premise that over 90% of all Barn Owl breeding sites in Britain are likely to be known by at least one person. Following extensive television, radio, magazine and journal coverage, it was estimated from readership, listening and viewing figures supplied that requests for Barn Owl data between 1982-1985 reached in excess of forty million people. Clearly this included those who would have read or heard about the project more than once, indeed repeated requests in the same journal were shown to be important in encouraging maximum public response.

The Survey Period

The full *Survey* was initially designed to run for two complete years, following the pilot survey in 1982. In the event it was increased a further year into 1985 providing an overall study period of four years. This was considered long enough to allow full coverage, and provide sufficient time to enable the verification of breeding records to take place. Since in the short-term Barn Owl numbers can be influenced markedly by temporary fluctuations in the vole population, it was also considered of prime importance to allow this *Survey* to extend over one complete vole cycle (3-4 years).

Recording Methods

Recording cards and questionnaires sought information concerning the month and year of observation, the precise location in terms of a four or six figure grid reference (alongside the name of the nearest farm or other identifying feature of the square), followed by the nearest village, town and county. If the birds were known to be nesting at the location specified, information was requested concerning the year of breeding and the nesting situation. Further data were sought about the major habitat and farm types within a 1 km radius of the site and, during the final two years, a key was provided to assist the observer in describing these categories as accurately as possible. The questionnaire also called for a subjective assessment as to whether the Barn Owl population in the study area had declined, remained static or increased over the last fifteen years. Finally, the recorders were asked if they had found any carcases and if so details relating to the location, date and circumstances of death (the final question was omitted from the recording card format).

Questionnaires were used for recording observations concerning a single site, whilst the recording card provided spaces for up to fifteen individual records. Special questionnaires were devised for The National Trust, Forestry Commission and Taxidermists' Guild together with other groups which undertook more specialised surveys.

To avoid the production of a separate set of recording cards and questionnaires marked 'confidential' for those recorders requesting secrecy, the *Survey* undertook that *all* breeding records would remain strictly confidential to the organiser.

The Use of Sample Areas

A considerable number of local and regional surveys were begun by licensed field workers following the start of the full *Survey* in 1983. In other areas, independent long-term population enquiries had been operating for a number of years. Whilst the study areas varied substantially in size, from entire counties to small groupings of 10-km squares, they formed the basis of a network of sample regions throughout the British Isles in which fieldworkers could reliably affirm that at least 80% of the breeding population had been located (Map 14).

The randomised locations and wide distribution of these sample areas provided an important means of assuring the quality of data received from other sources. This also provided an excellent means of establishing the comprehensiveness of the data which were being received on a nationwide basis. The method involved pinpointing the known breeding populations in each of the individual sample areas and comparing these with the number of sites notified as a consequence of blanket publicity.

The *Survey's* overall coverage in England, Wales and Scotland was found to be remarkably consistent when assessed on the basis of the known population density in each of the sample areas. The coverage level ranged from around 70-100%. Not unnaturally the lower coverage was apparent in areas where there was less human activity, such as Cornwall, parts of Devon, central Wales and north-eastern England. Whilst in all but the more remote regions of northern Scotland coverage was good, in Dumfries-shire and eastern Kirkcudbrightshire it was below 70%.

Data Sorting and Initial Checking

Eleven and a half thousand records were received over the four year period between 1982-1985. At the height of the *Survey* in 1984/85 100-200 records were received weekly. Reports which were in the form of letters, questionnaires or recording cards were scrutinised for

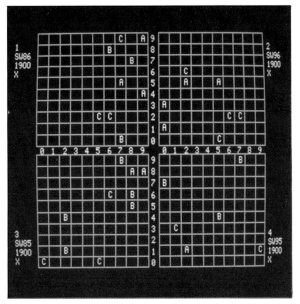

12. A single record displayed on the computer screen. Up to thirty items of information may be stored and subsequently sorted or retrieved from any of over 10,000 individual records.

13. Four adjacent 10 kilometre squares, each sub-divided into one kilometre squares, showing all records obtained in the Survey. Coded information is transferred automatically from the individual records.

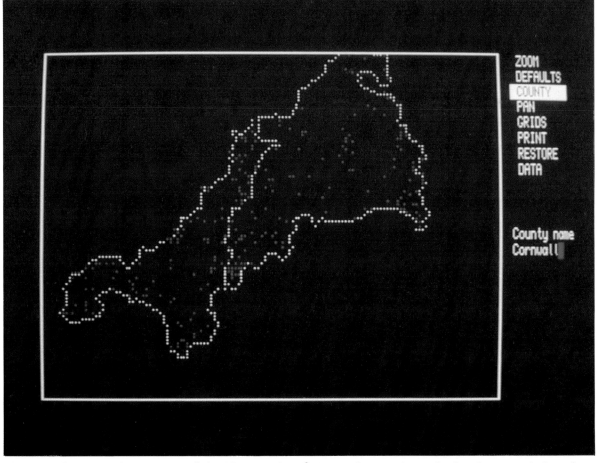

14. An outline map showing part of the Vice-counties of Cornwall. Records are displayed to a resolution of one kilometre.

validity in terms of correct species identification and locational accuracy. Approximately 15% were rejected through lack of sufficient detail or possible inaccuracy. In cases where immediate rejection may have led to the loss of important information, the data were referred back to the recorder for further details or on site verification.

It should be made clear at this point that records of the breeding of captive release birds were not included in the statistics used in the preparation of this report.

Upon delivery from the 'Freepost' address (arranged for the *Survey* in 1982), all responses involving the notification of nest sites or other more detailed replies were acknowledged. Records were allotted their appropriate grid references using the 1:50,000 (and 1:25,000) Ordnance Survey maps. The individual letters, questionnaires and recording cards were then allocated to the appropriate Vice-county files in surname order. Upon completion of the *Survey*, the data filled twenty-one volumes, each containing on average 250 individual communications. An additional six volumes contained data from local county organisers, general enquiries, and rejected records.

Nest site, breeding and non-breeding data were transferred to large scale biological maps (The Ray Society, Pub.No.146, Ordnance Survey 'Ten Mile' Map of Great Britain), as dots of differing colours for each of the four years (radius equivalent of 2 km.), coded to differentiate between breeding and non-breeding season records. This map was updated daily as each record was received prior to data capture and subsequent computer mapping in 1985 and 1986.

Data Capture and Computer Processing

By late 1984 it became clear that the mass of data which had been accumulated could only be processed satisfactorily by the use of a computer. After prolonged and careful consideration of the best ways of handling the problem, work began on writing the necessary programs and preparing the data in a form suitable for entry into the computer.

A data capture sheet was prepared and a list of codes (each comprising a group of two or three letters) was drawn up for the classification of habitats, farm types and other relevant data. This minimised the volume of keying into the computer and facilitated subsequent analysis and sorting, whilst the computer program itself would translate the codes into the full text for easy reading of each individual record.

At this stage each record which had survived previous checks was scrutinised again in detail and checked against the appropriate 1:50,000 Ordnance Survey map. Particular care was taken with regard to the map reference and the category of the observation (i.e. breeding record, breeding season or non-breeding season sighting). Any observation which could not reasonably be resolved to a four figure map reference or for which there was any doubt was rejected at this point. Additional information added to the record at this stage included the height above sea level and proximity to a waterway or wetland (if within 2 km.) and a motorway or railway (if within 3 km.). In all, facilities were available for the entry of up to thirty discrete pieces of information for each individual record. An illustration of such a single record is shown in Plate 12.

A separate computer file was maintained for each county, sub-divided into Watsonian Vice-counties. Facilities were available to sort, order, search or select items from the file according to any of the thirty fields entered and to print out such information which might from time to time be required.

At a later stage, the most important data for each breeding site were transferred to a spread sheet format and any possible duplicate records eliminated. By this time it had been appreciated that rainfall played an important part in nest site selection, and accordingly the mean annual rainfall at each site was added to the record after examination of the appropriate Meteorological Office rainfall map (Meteorological Office 1977).

To assist in the assessment of the breeding population, a computer program was developed to display the records at a resolution of one km., in blocks of four adjacent ten kilometre squares as illustrated in Plate 13. To facilitate rapid examination of this display it was programmed to pan in either horizontal or vertical direction whilst maintaining a block of four adjacent squares. Categories and/or years could be displayed individually, or, more usefully, all records could be diplayed simultaneously. In the latter case, B records (breeding season sightings) would overwrite C records (non-breeding season sightings), and A records (nest sites) would overwrite B records, thus displaying the highest value record for each kilometre square.

Finally, to give an overall view of the situation in any one county, the computer could display an outline map of the county together with all the records for one or more categories shown in the form of single dots (Plate 14).

For the technically minded, the equipment used comprised a Sinclair QL computer with twin 3.5 inch disc drives and 640K memory, colour monitor and Taxan Kaga KP-810 dot matrix printer. Some programs were based on Psion 'Archive', 'Abacus', 'Easel' and 'Quill' software, whilst other facilities, notably the programs for mapping and the display of 10-km squares were specially written for the Barn Owl Survey.

As this report goes to press, work has started on a computer simulation of Barn Owl breeding success and population levels. It is hoped that this work, using the mass of data accumulated over the last five years, will shed further light on our understanding of the ecology of the Barn Owl.

Data Verification

The major justifiable criticism of any survey, especially one involving the Barn Owl, is the possibility of species misidentification. Information received from non-naturalist sources must be viewed with caution since much confusion can arise concerning the identification of the Barn Owl with the Tawny Owl, Little Owl and in Scotland, the Short-eared Owl. Illustrations were therefore used in the majority of the publicised requests for data to assist the reader with some aid to correct identification.

Of the 10,000 different records which had been accepted following the earlier data checking process 50% were from non-naturalist sources. Of the remaining 5,000, the majority originated from farmers, gamekeepers, foresters and landowners. 3,000 of these were either obtained from questionnaires completed following personal interviews at the Barn Owl Survey stands at the CLA Game Fair (1983-1986), or from reliable sources which were so specific in detail that further verification was deemed unnecessary. Of the final 2,000 which included 600 nest sites, verification was obtained by on site inspection by a local specialist, telephone interview or by requesting, through the post, a single pellet collected from beneath the nest site in question. This last technique proved a simple but nevertheless invaluable means of confirming correct species identification.

By the end of 1986 and the completion of nest site verification the maximum misidentification error on the total of 2,699 nest records was calculated to be below 1%.

A second technique further increased confidence in this figure. In Hertfordshire where less than 10 pairs of Barn Owls now remain, all reports which passed the preliminary checking procedure were investigated in the field. In spite of an initial rejection rate of approximately 25% on receipt, because of obvious misidentification or vague reports, only 1.5% of the remainder were found to be false following site investigation.

This was particularly encouraging in a county where large numbers of both Tawny and Little Owls are present and a high level of species misidentification might well have been anticipated. Similar investigations in other regions confirmed this encouraging figure.

Final confirmation of the exceptionally low level of error arising as a result of species misidentification, emerged during the nest site analysis undertaken towards the end of the *Survey*. It was based on the observation that throughout the western regions of Devon, Wales, Cheshire, Lancashire, Westmorland and Cumberland where 391 known nest sites were reported, only thirty-eight tree nesting Barn Owls were found. Indeed, in south Devon (Vice-county 3), not one tree nest site was reported. Since the Tawny Owl rarely nests within buildings in Britain (less than 1% on Nest Record Cards, Glue pers.comm.), the figure would suggest that at worst the misidentification figure could have been 9.7%. However, all but six of these tree sites were in fact notified by expert field workers. As a result the maximum identification error throughout western regions was unlikely to exceed 1.5%.

Since there was little reason to expect any increased level of inaccuracy elsewhere in Britain, this inbuilt method of verification, which could not have originally been foreseen, provided the most conclusive evidence that the original checking procedures were more than adequate to weed out false records and that any errors arising in the final analyses could be considered negligible.

Data Storage

A complete set of computer files comprising all the data for each record (as shown in Plate 12), will be deposited with the Biological Records Centre at the Institute of Terrestrial Ecology, Monks Wood Experimental Station, Cambs.

Calculation of Population

However carefully a survey is undertaken, limitations are imposed which need to be taken into account when presenting the final statistics and conclusions. On this basis it would clearly have been unjustified to quote absolute population densities in each individual square for a notoriously elusive species whose numbers fluctuate annually. Additionally, some movement of individual breeding pairs invariably occurs over a period of four years, which can also have the potential for prejudicing the calculation of local population totals.

In order to record the population density on a legitimate basis Barn Owl abundance within each 10-km square has been shown within defined ranges. However these ranges, especially the higher ones, do not necessarily reflect the extent of population uncertainty within squares, but provide a means of limiting the number of symbols needed to illustrate nationwide population levels in map form. The ranges selected for the present *Survey* have also purposely been chosen to allow direct comparison with the census results in 1932, following conversion of these historic data from 10-mile squares to 10-km squares.

Computerised data handling allowed the scrutiny of approximately 350,000 1-km squares such that population levels within the above ranges could accurately be ascribed for most of the 3,862 10-km squares in the British Isles. The major exception occurred in the Republic of Ireland where countrywide coverage was considered too low for reliable estimates to be made on this basis.

Breeding densities were calculated from the number of confirmed breeding records within each 10-km square, together with the groupings of other breeding season records of pairs of birds or single birds, which were separated in the square by distances of 2-3 km. This distance generally represents the ranging limits of the species over most habitat types, and local field studies revealed that birds which were observed consistently over a period of years were, on closer scrutiny, invariably found to be nesting. Criteria used to judge 'confirmed breeding' were the same as that used for the Atlas of Breeding Birds of Britain and Ireland (Sharrock 1976).

Abundance within the defined ranges was therefore categorised and mapped on this basis throughout the British Isles. In those squares where the numbers of birds present were on the borderline of two ranges, the final population density was recorded in favour of the higher range in those areas where coverage was known to be less thorough. The lower range was selected where coverage was considered complete.

BARN OWL SURVEY OF BRITAIN AND IRELAND 1982-1985
NEST SITE SUMMARY   —   ENGLAND

County:	Cornw	Devon	Somer	Dorset	Wight	Hants	Sussex	Kent	Surrey	Essex	Herts	Middx	Berks	Oxfrd
Farm bldngs														
On bales	6	12	3	5	1	18	15	4	0	5	0	0	2	0
Nest box	3	7	2	2	0	2	8	1	0	1	0	0	0	1
In roof	5	15	6	3	0	4	5	5	4	1	0	0	2	1
Water tank	1	0	0	0	0	1	2	1	0	0	0	0	0	0
On wall	6	6	2	5	0	1	1	0	2	2	0	0	1	0
Not specified	30	48	13	18	3	26	25	4	0	10	0	0	5	7
Total:	51	88	26	28	4	51	56	15	6	18	0	0	8	9
Domestic bldngs														
In chimney	1	3	2	1	0	0	0	1	0	1	0	0	0	1
Nest box	2	0	0	0	0	0	2	1	0	0	0	0	0	1
Roof/ceiling	2	2	0	1	0	1	0	3	1	0	0	0	1	1
On wall	0	0	1	0	0	1	5	2	0	1	0	0	0	0
Not specified	5	0	0	0	3	1	1	4	0	2	0	1	0	1
Total:	8	5	4	2	3	3	8	11	1	4	0	1	1	4
Misc structures														
Bridge	2	1	0	0	0	0	2	0	0	0	0	0	0	0
Church in use	1	3	1	1	0	2	2	3	0	0	0	0	0	1
Castle	0	1	0	1	0	0	0	0	0	0	0	0	0	0
Disused church	0	0	0	0	0	0	0	0	0	0	0	0	0	0
Dovecote	0	0	0	0	0	5	3	0	0	0	0	0	0	0
Industrial	2	1	1	0	0	0	3	2	1	5	1	0	0	1
Mine	2	0	0	0	0	0	0	0	0	0	0	0	0	0
Oasthouse	0	0	0	0	0	0	0	5	0	0	0	0	0	0
Pump house	0	0	0	0	0	0	2	0	0	0	0	0	0	0
Mill	1	1	1	0	0	0	1	0	2	0	0	0	0	1
Total:	8	5	1	3	0	7	13	10	2	5	1	0	0	4
Total M	67	98	31	32	6	61	77	29	9	24	0	1	9	14
Cliff/Quarry	1	0	1	0	0	0	0	0	0	0	0	0	0	1
Cave	0	0	0	0	0	0	0	0	0	0	0	0	0	0
Total C	1	0	1	0	0	0	0	0	0	0	0	0	0	1
Not specified	5	17	18	13	3	11	7	5	1	14	1	0	2	16
Tree														
Ash	2	1	5	4	3	1	0	2	0	0	0	1	0	3
Beech	0	0	5	1	1	1	3	1	1	0	0	1	0	0
Chestnut	0	0	0	0	0	0	1	1	0	0	0	0	0	2
Elm	11	4	4	3	8	2	4	0	1	1	0	0	1	2
Pine	2	0	0	7	0	0	4	0	1	0	0	0	0	0
Walnut	1	0	0	0	0	0	0	0	2	0	0	0	0	1
Oak	0	2	8	3	5	0	4	7	6	2	0	0	1	1
Poplar	0	0	0	0	0	0	1	0	2	0	0	0	0	0
Birch	0	2	0	0	0	0	0	0	1	0	0	0	0	0
Sycamore	1	0	0	2	0	0	0	0	0	0	0	0	0	0
Willow	0	0	5	5	9	2	1	3	0	0	0	0	0	0
Not specified	7	4	4	2	9	5	3	2	4	1	0	0	4	3
Total T	23	4	26	39	14	24	17	11	13	9	24	4	0	13
TOTAL SITES	96	119	76	78	59	89	95	47	19	62	6	0	24	41

NEST SITE SUMMARY   —   ENGLAND

County:	Bucks	Suffk	Norfk	Cambs	Beds	Hunts	Nhant	Glos	Mon	Heref	Worcs	Warks	Staff	Salop	Lincs
Farm bldngs															
On bales	0	3	5	0	1	0	2	3	1	0	0	2	1	1	7
Nest box	0	1	1	1	1	1	3	0	0	0	0	0	0	2	12
In roof	1	0	2	3	0	1	0	1	0	0	0	3	0	2	7
Water tank	0	0	0	0	0	0	0	0	0	0	0	0	0	0	1
On wall	0	1	2	2	1	0	1	1	0	2	1	0	0	1	1
Not specified	6	23	28	10	1	6	6	6	1	2	2	4	12	6	39
Total:	7	28	38	14	1	11	10	2	4	7	10	15	17	70
Domestic buildings															
In chimney	0	0	1	1	0	0	1	0	0	0	0	0	1	2	5
Nest box	0	1	0	0	0	0	0	1	0	0	0	1	0	1	0
Roof/ceiling	0	0	0	1	0	0	1	0	0	0	1	0	0	0	5
On wall	0	0	1	0	0	0	1	0	0	1	0	1	0	0	0
Not specified	0	0	6	3	0	0	2	0	0	0	0	2	1	4	11
Total:	0	0	7	3	0	0	1	1	0	1	1	0	2	0	21
Misc structures															
Bridge	1	1	1	1	0	0	1	0	0	0	0	0	0	1	0
Church in use	2	3	1	0	0	0	0	0	1	0	1	2	1	0	5
Castle	0	0	0	0	0	0	0	0	0	0	0	0	0	0	0
Disused church	0	0	0	0	0	0	1	0	0	0	0	0	0	1	2
Dovecote	0	0	1	0	0	0	1	0	2	0	1	1	0	2	1
Industrial	0	0	2	0	0	0	1	2	4	0	0	2	0	2	7
Mine	0	0	0	0	0	0	0	1	0	1	0	0	0	0	2
Oasthouse	0	0	0	0	0	0	0	0	0	0	0	0	0	0	0
Pump house	0	1	0	0	0	0	0	0	0	0	0	0	0	0	0
Mill	1	1	1	1	0	0	0	1	0	1	0	0	1	1	2
Total:	2	3	7	2	0	0	5	1	5	1	1	4	1	4	17
Total M	9	31	52	19	4	1	14	13	7	5	8	14	18	21	108
Cliff/Quarry	0	0	0	0	0	0	0	0	0	0	0	0	0	0	0
Cave	0	0	0	0	0	0	0	0	0	0	0	0	0	0	0
Total C	0	0	0	0	0	0	0	0	0	0	0	0	0	0	0
Not specified	0	23	26	9	1	0	7	5	3	3	4	4	14	7	24
Tree															
Ash	1	1	4	0	0	1	1	0	0	0	1	2	1	2	12
Beech	0	1	1	0	0	0	1	0	0	0	1	1	2	1	1
Chestnut	0	1	0	8	2	4	1	0	0	0	0	3	0	0	16
Elm	1	19	12	0	5	0	1	0	0	0	0	0	1	0	0
Pine	0	1	1	1	0	0	2	0	0	0	0	0	1	0	0
Walnut	0	22	18	1	2	1	0	7	0	2	3	3	1	8	3
Oak	1	22	18	1	2	1	0	4	0	2	3	0	0	1	0
Poplar	1	0	0	0	0	0	0	0	0	0	0	0	0	0	0
Birch	0	0	0	0	0	0	0	0	0	0	0	0	0	0	1
Sycamore	0	0	0	0	0	0	0	2	0	0	0	0	0	0	0
Willow	1	2	13	6	1	0	2	3	0	0	0	1	1	4	23
Not specified	3	29	13	6	1	0	2	3	0	0	0	1	1	4	23
Total T	8	73	51	17	5	7	10	9	0	6	5	8	7	18	58
TOTAL SITES	17	127	129	45	10	8	31	27	10	14	17	26	39	46	190

NEST SITE SUMMARY   –   ENGLAND

County:	Leics	Notts	Derby	Chesh	Lancs	Yorks	Durhe	Nthmb	Clevt	Welnd	Cumb	IOM	ENGTOTAL
Farm buildings													
On bales	1	2	4	0	1	15	0	0	0	0	6	0	151
Nest box	0	0	2	17	1	2	0	0	1	0	3	0	70
In roof	0	2	6	3	0	5	0	0	0	0	1	0	85
Water tank	0	0	0	0	0	2	0	0	0	0	2	0	13
On wall	0	1	0	1	0	4	0	0	1	0	5	0	38
Not specified	5	8	17	52	52	35	1	4	3	1	10	3	488
Total:	6	11	29	54	63	63	2	4	3	3	27	3	845
Domestic bldngs													
In chimney	1	0	0	0	0	3	0	0	0	0	0	0	23
Nest box	0	0	0	1	0	0	1	0	0	0	0	0	0
Roof/ceiling	1	0	0	0	0	1	0	1	1	0	3	0	30
On wall	0	0	1	0	0	0	0	0	0	0	0	0	1
Not specified	0	0	3	3	2	2	0	2	2	0	3	0	53
Total:	2	0	4	4	2	6	0	3	3	2	6	0	107
Misc structures													
Bridge	0	1	0	2	2	1	1	0	0	0	0	0	13
Church in use	1	1	1	1	1	1	1	0	0	0	0	0	33
Castle	0	0	0	0	0	2	1	0	0	0	0	0	3
Disused church	0	0	1	1	1	0	0	0	1	0	4	0	6
Dovecote	0	0	3	0	1	5	0	0	0	0	0	0	16
Industrial	1	2	3	3	0	7	0	1	1	0	4	0	64
Mine	0	0	0	0	0	4	0	0	1	0	0	0	3
Oasthouse	0	0	0	0	0	0	0	0	0	0	0	0	7
Pump house	0	1	1	1	0	0	0	0	0	0	0	0	1
Mill	0	1	0	3	2	2	1	0	0	1	0	0	17
Total M	2	3	5	7	8	19	3	5	7	8	19	3	163
	10	14	34	20	64	88	3	5	7	8	19	3	1115
Cliff/Quarry	0	0	3	0	0	1	0	0	0	0	2	0	9
Cave	0	0	0	3	0	0	0	0	0	0	2	0	0
Total C	0	0	3	0	0	1	0	0	0	0	2	0	9
Not specified	3	5	9	4	9	50	2	1	1	2	4	0	342
Tree													
Ash	1	2	1	1	0	10	0	2	0	0	0	0	66
Beech	0	0	1	1	0	0	0	0	0	0	0	0	11
Chestnut	0	0	0	0	0	0	0	0	0	0	0	0	4
Elm	0	9	0	1	0	3	0	0	0	0	0	0	142
Pine	0	0	0	0	0	0	0	0	0	0	0	0	4
Walnut	0	0	1	0	0	0	0	0	0	0	0	0	7
Oak	2	5	0	0	0	1	0	0	0	0	4	0	141
Poplar	0	3	3	0	0	0	0	0	0	0	0	0	9
Birch	0	0	0	0	0	1	0	0	0	0	0	0	1
Sycamore	0	0	0	0	0	2	0	0	0	0	0	0	23
Willow	0	5	0	0	0	0	0	0	0	0	0	0	6
Not specified	0	22	1	1	1	19	0	5	0	0	1	0	186
Total T	3	22	11	4	2	35	0	7	0	0	5	0	600
TOTAL SITES	16	41	57	26	74	174	6	6	15	20	48	3	2066

NEST SITE SUMMARY   –   WALES

County:	Glam	Brecn	Radnr	Carml	Pembk	Cardg	Montg	Meron	Carnv	Denb	Flint	Angle	WALESTOTAL
Farm bldngs													
On bales	0	0	0	0	0	1	0	1	0	4	0	2	8
Nest box	0	0	1	0	1	1	2	2	2	0	0	22	26
In roof	0	0	0	0	1	1	2	0	2	0	0	0	7
Water tank	0	0	0	0	0	0	0	1	0	0	0	0	2
On wall	0	0	4	0	6	1	2	1	1	5	0	0	2
Not specified	8	0	0	0	6	5	5	4	5	9	2	2	46
Total:	8	0	5	6	7	8	4	6	8	9	1	28	91
Domestic bldngs													
In chimney	0	0	0	0	1	0	0	2	2	0	0	2	5
Nest box	0	0	0	0	0	0	0	0	0	0	0	0	0
Roof/ceiling	0	0	0	0	0	3	0	0	0	0	0	1	4
On wall	0	0	2	0	5	5	1	0	0	1	0	0	0
Not specified	0	0	0	0	1	8	0	0	2	1	0	3	9
Total:	0	0	2	0	1	8	1	0	2	1	0	3	18
Misc structures													
Bridge	1	0	0	0	0	0	0	0	0	0	0	0	0
Church in use	0	0	0	0	0	1	0	0	0	1	0	0	3
Castle	0	0	0	0	0	1	0	0	0	0	0	0	0
Disused church	0	0	0	0	1	0	0	0	0	0	0	0	1
Dovecote	0	0	0	0	0	0	0	0	1	0	0	0	0
Industrial	2	0	0	0	1	0	1	0	0	1	0	1	4
Mine	0	0	0	0	0	0	0	0	0	0	0	0	0
Oasthouse	0	0	0	0	0	0	0	0	0	0	0	0	0
Pump house	0	0	0	0	0	0	0	0	0	0	0	0	0
Mill	3	0	0	2	2	1	0	0	0	1	1	1	9
Total M	11	0	7	6	10	17	5	6	10	11	3	32	118
Cliff/Quarry	0	0	0	0	0	0	2	0	0	0	0	1	3
Cave	0	0	0	0	0	0	0	0	2	0	0	0	0
Total C	0	0	0	0	0	0	2	0	0	0	0	1	3
Not specified	0	1	4	4	5	1	2	2	5	0	0	4	28
Tree													
Ash	0	0	0	0	0	1	0	0	0	0	0	0	1
Beech	0	0	0	0	0	0	0	0	0	0	0	0	0
Chestnut	0	0	0	0	0	4	0	0	0	0	0	0	0
Elm	0	0	0	0	0	0	0	0	0	0	0	0	0
Pine	0	0	0	0	0	0	0	0	0	0	0	0	0
Walnut	0	0	0	0	0	0	0	0	0	0	0	0	0
Oak	0	0	0	0	1	1	0	0	1	1	0	0	3
Poplar	0	0	0	0	0	1	0	0	0	0	0	0	0
Birch	0	0	0	0	0	0	0	0	0	0	0	0	0
Sycamore	0	0	0	0	0	0	0	0	0	0	0	0	0
Walnut	2	1	1	0	1	1	1	0	1	1	0	0	6
Not specified	2	1	1	0	2	1	1	0	1	1	0	0	10
Total T	13	2	12	10	17	19	8	10	16	12	3	37	159
TOTAL SITES	13	2	12	10	17	19	8	10	16	12	3	37	159

NEST SITE SUMMARY — SCOTLAND

County:	Dumfs	Kircu	Wigtn	Ayr	Renfr	Lanrk	Peebl	Selk	Roxbu	Berwk	Loth	Fife	Stirl	Perth	Angus
Farm bldngs															
On bales	8	7	6	0	0	2	0	0	1	0	0	0	0	0	0
Nest box	0	3	4	2	0	2	0	0	1	0	0	0	0	0	0
In roof	2	4	4	5	0	0	0	0	0	1	0	0	0	0	0
Water tank	1	0	0	1	0	0	0	0	1	0	0	0	0	0	0
On wall	1	3	4	0	0	0	0	0	1	2	0	0	1	0	0
Not specified	23	9	4	4	0	0	1	0	2	2	1	2	1	2	1
Total:	34	26	22	12	0	2	0	2	3	5	1	3	3	3	0
Domestic bldngs															
In chimney	3	2	1	1	0	0	0	0	1	0	0	1	0	1	0
Nest box	0	1	0	0	0	0	0	0	0	0	0	0	0	0	0
Roof/ceiling	3	3	18	3	0	0	0	0	0	0	0	0	0	0	0
On wall	1	0	2	0	0	1	0	0	0	0	1	0	0	0	0
Not specified	9	6	3	1	0	0	0	0	0	1	0	0	1	0	0
Total:	16	12	28	5	0	1	0	0	1	1	1	1	1	2	0
Misc structures															
Bridge	0	0	0	0	0	0	0	0	0	0	0	0	0	1	0
Church in use	1	0	3	1	0	0	0	0	0	0	0	0	0	0	1
Castle	0	3	1	0	1	0	0	0	1	0	0	0	0	0	0
Disused church	0	0	0	0	0	0	0	0	0	0	0	0	0	0	0
Dovecote	0	0	1	0	0	0	0	0	0	0	0	0	0	0	0
Industrial	0	0	0	1	0	0	0	0	0	0	0	0	0	0	0
Mine	0	0	0	0	0	0	0	0	1	0	0	0	0	0	0
Oasthouse	0	0	0	0	0	0	0	0	0	0	0	0	0	0	0
Pump house	1	0	0	0	0	0	0	0	0	0	0	0	0	0	0
Mill	0	0	1	1	1	0	0	0	0	0	1	0	0	0	1
Total:	2	3	3	1	0	0	0	0	2	0	1	0	0	2	0
Total M	52	41	53	18	1	3	1	0	5	4	1	3	2	2	0
Cliff/Quarry	0	0	0	0	1	0	0	0	4	0	0	0	0	1	0
Cave	0	0	0	1	0	0	0	0	0	0	0	0	0	0	0
Total C	0	0	1	1	1	0	0	0	4	0	0	0	0	1	0
Not specified	4	9	2	4	1	2	0	0	4	0	1	4	0	5	1
Tree															
Ash	0	0	0	0	0	0	0	0	1	0	0	1	0	0	0
Beech	1	0	0	0	0	0	0	0	1	0	0	1	0	0	1
Chestnut	0	0	0	0	0	0	0	0	0	0	0	0	0	0	0
Elm	0	0	0	0	0	0	0	0	1	0	0	1	0	1	1
Pine	0	0	0	0	0	0	0	0	0	0	0	0	0	0	0
Walnut	0	0	0	0	0	0	0	0	0	0	0	0	0	0	0
Oak	2	0	0	0	1	0	0	0	0	0	0	0	0	0	0
Poplar	0	0	0	0	0	0	0	0	0	1	0	0	0	0	0
Birch	1	0	0	0	0	0	0	0	0	0	0	0	0	0	0
Sycamore	0	0	0	0	0	0	0	0	0	0	0	0	0	0	1
Willow	0	2	2	0	0	0	0	0	0	0	0	0	0	0	0
Not specified	1	2	3	1	0	0	0	0	0	0	0	1	0	3	0
Total T	5	2	2	2	0	0	0	0	0	2	0	1	0	11	3
TOTAL SITES	61	52	58	25	2	5	2	0	9	6	2	8	2	11	3

NEST SITE SUMMARY — SCOTLAND / TOTALS

	Kinud	Aberd	Banff	Moray	Inver	Argyl	Dunbt	Butes	WIsls	R&C	Suthd	Caith		Scot (count)	Sited	W&NZ	TOTAL
Farm bldngs																	
On bales	0	0	0	1	0	1	1	0	0	0	0	0		24	2	159	185
Nest box	0	0	0	1	1	0	0	0	0	1	0	0		15	2	94	111
In roof	0	0	0	0	1	0	0	0	0	0	0	0		17	2	92	111
Water tank	0	0	0	0	0	0	0	0	0	0	0	0		1	0	15	16
On wall	1	2	0	0	0	1	0	0	0	0	0	0		14	0	40	54
Not specified	2	2	1	1	1	2	1	5	3	1	0	2		66	6	534	606
Total:	4	4	1	2	2	3	5	5	5	3	0	2		137	10	936	1083
Domestic bldngs																	
In chimney	0	0	0	0	0	0	0	0	0	0	0	0		13	2	28	43
Nest box	0	0	0	0	0	0	0	0	0	0	0	0		1	0	0	1
Roof/ceiling	0	0	1	0	1	0	0	0	0	0	0	0		29	0	34	63
On wall	0	1	0	0	0	0	0	1	0	0	0	0		3	2	1	6
Not specified	1	0	0	0	0	2	1	0	0	1	0	0		25	18	62	105
Total:	0	1	1	0	1	2	1	1	0	1	0	0		71	22	125	218
Misc structures																	
Bridge	1	0	0	1	1	1	0	0	0	1	0	0		1	0	13	14
Church in use	0	0	0	0	0	0	0	0	0	0	0	0		3	2	36	41
Castle	0	1	1	1	1	0	0	0	0	0	0	0		8	56	3	67
Disused church	0	0	0	0	0	0	0	0	0	0	0	0		1	0	7	9
Dovecote	0	0	0	1	0	0	1	0	0	0	0	0		1	0	7	18
Industrial	0	0	0	0	0	0	0	0	0	0	0	0		1	2	17	72
Mine	0	0	0	1	1	0	0	0	0	0	0	0		2	2	68	5
Oasthouse	0	0	0	0	0	0	0	0	0	0	0	0		2	2	3	5
Pump house	0	0	0	0	0	0	0	0	0	0	0	0		0	0	7	7
Mill	0	0	0	0	0	0	0	0	0	1	0	0		4	2	1	1
Total:	1	0	1	0	1	1	0	1	0	1	0	1		21	64	172	257
Total M	5	5	3	2	6	5	7	6	1	3	0	2		229	96	1233	1558
Cliff/Quarry	1	0	0	1	5	0	6	7	0	1	1	0		24	2	12	38
Cave	0	0	0	0	0	5	0	0	0	0	0	0		4	0	0	4
Total C	1	0	0	1	5	0	6	7	0	1	0	0		28	2	12	42
Not specified	0	7	2	1	4	7	0	6	1	3	0	0		68	7	370	445
Tree																	
Ash	0	0	0	0	0	0	0	0	0	0	0	0		4	0	67	71
Beech	0	0	0	0	1	0	0	0	0	0	0	1		6	3	11	20
Chestnut	0	0	0	0	0	0	0	0	0	0	0	0		0	0	4	4
Elm	0	0	0	2	0	0	0	0	0	0	0	1		2	4	142	148
Pine	0	0	0	0	0	0	0	0	0	0	0	0		0	0	4	4
Walnut	0	0	0	0	0	0	0	0	0	0	0	0		0	0	7	7
Oak	0	0	0	0	1	0	0	0	0	0	0	0		3	4	144	151
Poplar	0	0	0	0	0	0	0	0	0	0	0	0		1	0	9	9
Birch	0	0	0	0	0	0	0	0	0	0	0	0		0	0	1	2
Sycamore	0	0	0	0	0	0	0	0	0	0	0	0		1	0	6	7
Willow	0	0	0	0	0	0	0	0	0	0	0	0		0	1	23	23
Not specified	0	0	0	1	4	0	0	0	0	0	0	3		12	4	192	208
Total T	0	0	0	0	5	0	0	0	0	0	0	2		25	19	610	654
TOTAL SITES	6	12	5	3	6	23	5	19	14	5	0	2		350	124	2225	2699

CHANNEL ISLANDS — Jersey 9 (80% trees—mainly elm), Guernsey 13 (50% trees—mainly elm), Sark 4 (50% trees), Alderney 6 (70% cliffs/quarries).

APPENDIX IV

Distribution of 547 Barn Owls Preserved by Williams and Sons out of a total of 739 on their Books during the Ten Years 1887–1896.

Donegal	4	Queens Co. (Laois)	24	Meath	28	Galway	17
Derry	0	Wicklow	33	Louth	19	Roscommon	10
Antrim	1	Wexford	16	Dublin	79	Mayo	10
Tyrone	8	Carlow	23	Kildare	30	Sligo	3
Down	3	Kilkenny	40	Kings Co. (Offaly)	22	Leitrim	3
Armagh	1	Tipperary	61				
Monaghan	7	Waterford	4				
Fermanagh	11	Cork	5	Ulster	40		
Cavan	5	Kerry	12	Leinster	337		
Longford	4	Limerick	21	Munster	122		
Westmeath	19	Clare	19	Connaught	43		

APPENDIX V

BARN OWL PROJECT – POST-MORTEM FINDINGS

By J E Cooper FRCVS
Department of Pathology
Royal College of Surgeons of England
35-43 Lincoln's Inn Fields, London WC2A 3PN

A total of 57 Barn Owls *Tyto alba* has been examined in our laboratory since October 1982. Of these the majority were submitted as part of The Hawk Trust's Barn Owl Survey. All birds received were investigated in an identical fashion, following a standard technique, regardless of their age or whether they were free-living ('wild'), casualties which had been tended, or captive birds. Each owl received a full gross post-mortem examination coupled with laboratory tests (bacteriology, parasitology, histopathology) as appropriate. Some birds were radiographed (x-rayed) in order to detect fractures or to investigate the skeletal system. Finally all carcases have been retained so that they can be submitted to another laboratory for chemical analysis.

The emphasis in this study has not been on the cause of death. This is often important but may not be the most significant finding. An owl might, for example, have died as a result of colliding with a vehicle but the discovery of internal parasites or of pathological changes in the kidneys may prove of more value, in the long run, in elucidating the factors that might contribute to disease or death in this species.

Major findings in the 57 owls were as follows (in some cases one bird showed two or more):

Road accident or other trauma	24 birds
Inanition ('starvation')	14 birds
Coccidia	7 birds
Fatty liver	3 birds
Shock	2 birds
Dehydration	1 bird
Chilling	1 bird
Peritonitis	1 bird
Pancreatitis	1 bird
No diagnosis	6 birds
Investigations still in progress	10 birds

A number of interesting points have emerged from this study and some are being pursued. For example, the role of coccidia (protozoan parasites of the intestine) is unclear: further work is needed to ascertain whether they cause illness or death in their own right or are only secondary to other factors.

I am grateful to those who have submitted owls to me for examination and to The Hawk Trust for some financial assistance towards the work.

APPENDIX VI

THE CONSTRUCTION AND SITING OF NESTBOXES FOR BARN OWLS

Barn Owls will often accept nestboxes when they are positioned at previously known roosting or nesting sites in ruined buildings, relatively undisturbed barns and other lightly used farm structures. Permanent access into the building must however exist through a doorway, window or ventilation slit and this entrance should preferably be not less than 6" wide by 6" high. Ideally, Barn Owls prefer to have at least two means of wide entry and escape together with an uninterrupted flight path to the box.

Nestboxes are simple to construct and an example is shown. (Box sizes are approximate, but should not be much smaller than indicated). For interior use, a modified tea chest is quite satisfactory after the metal edging has been knocked flat and the lining paper removed. Special boxes, or those which are likely to be exposed to moisture, can be made of 6 mm or 9 mm exterior quality plywood. A single outside panel or inspection hatch can be secured in such a way as to allow removal every few years so that accumulated debris can be discarded. A platform outside the box should be provided to help prevent the emerging owlets from falling to the ground. Ten-gallon plastic drums can be used although they are prone to heavy condensation and rapid heat loss. For this reason they are less suitable in damp or exposed situations.

(a) Purpose-made boxes which are very heavy can be difficult to erect. Erection in hay barns is best accomplished when the building is full of bales, allowing easier access to the roof space. It is advantageous to retain a stack of bales beneath and around the nestbox area from January to July, and if at all possible throughout the year. This provides additional seclusion and encourages Barn Owls to select these artificial sites. Alternatively, tunnels can be constructed, about three bales deep, in the face of a bale stack to provide natural nesting quarters.

(b) In timber, stone or brick barns, boxes are best nailed or screwed high up in a secluded area of the barn, preferably on an inside gable away from any major light source and the prevailing wind. A sprinkling of dry peat or pellet debris can be placed inside the box.

(c) In more modern open steel or concrete and asbestos barns, fixing of boxes is often more difficult. It is sometimes necessary to nail long wooden spars to the box which can then be wired or roped to the trusses in the darkest part of the barn roof against the side panels of the building. (See nestbox plans for more permanent fixing and for use by farm building manufacturers.)

(d) In food storage barns, a nestbox can be backed up against the access hole on the barn wall to prevent the owl's entry into the building itself.

(e) Alternatively, specially designed Barn Owl 'lofts' can be included in the apex of buildings when modernisation or conversion is likely to result in the loss of Barn Owls from such sites.

(f) Boxes should be erected in an upright position in trees, but are usually only successful in regions where trees are the preferred site (see Map 6). Boxes can also be positioned within hollow tree stumps.

If a box is thought to be in use, it should be observed discreetly from a safe distance, since desertion, especially of eggs and small young, can easily occur, especially at newly occupied sites.

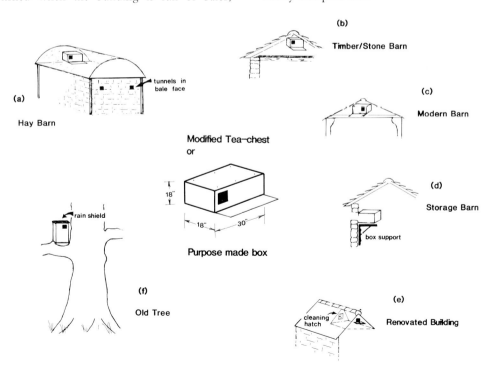

(a) Hay Barn — tunnels in bale face

(b) Timber/Stone Barn

(c) Modern Barn

(d) Storage Barn — box support

(e) Renovated Building — cleaning hatch

(f) Old Tree — rain shield

Modified Tea-chest or Purpose made box — 18" / 18" / 30"

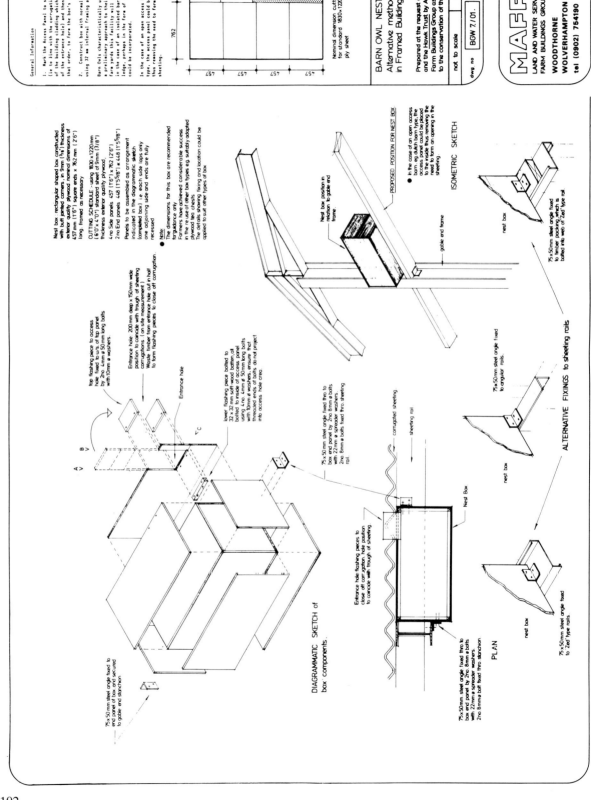

General Information

1. Mark the Access Panel to suit site conditions (ie in line with the corrugation peaks on the inside of the building cladding which are to form the edges of the entrance hole) and then make cuts A, B & C in that order, to form the box's entry hole.

2. Construct box with normal butt jointed corners using 32 mm internal framing as necessary.

Barn Owls characteristically use a landing ledge as a preliminary approach to their nest site. In most farm yards this facility will already exist. However in the case of an isolated barn gable, a landing ledge, perhaps in the form of a cantilever bracket, could be incorporated.

In the case of an open access barn eg. dutch barn type, the access panel could be placed to the inside thus removing the need to form an opening in the sheeting.

Nominal dimension cutting diagram for standard 1830×1220mm (6'0"×4'0") ply sheet

877   877
19
448
762
score
457   457   457   457

Nest box: rectangular shaped box constructed with butt jointed corners, in 9mm (³/₈") thickness exterior quality plywood which are to form the edges of the entrance hole dimensions of 457mm (1'6") square ends × 762mm (2'6") long, framed as necessary.

CUTTING SCHEDULE - using 1830×1220mm (6'0"×4'0") standard sheet of 9mm (3/8") thickness exterior quality plywood.

4 no Side panels 457 (1'6") × 762 (2'6")
2 no End panels 448 (1'5⁹/₁₆") × 448 (1'5⁹/₁₆")

Panels to be assembled as arrangement indicated in the diagrammatic sketch (completed box) i.e. each side laps only one adjoining side and ends are fully recessed

● Note
The dimensions for this box are recommended for guidance only.
Farmers have achieved considerable success in the re use of other box types eg. suitably adopted plywood tea chests.
The details showing fixing and location could be applied to suit other types of box

top flashing piece to access hole fixed to u/s of top panel by 2no 4mm ⌀ 50mm long bolts with 10mm ⌀ washers.

Entrance hole 200 mm deep × 150mm wide position to coincide with trough of sheeting corrugations. (on site measurement)
Waste timber from entrance hole cut in half to form flashing pieces to close off corrugation

Entrance hole

lower flashing piece bolted to 32 × 32 mm soft-wood batten, all bolted to inside of access panel using 4 no 4mm ⌀ 50mm long bolts with 10mm ⌀ washers, ensure that threaded ends of bolts do not project into access hole area.

A▷ B▷ ▷C

75 × 50 mm steel angle fixed thro to end panel of box and secured to gable end stanchion

DIAGRAMMATIC SKETCH of box components.

PROPOSED POSITION FOR NEST BOX

● In the case of an open access barn eg. dutch barn type, the access panel could be placed to the inside thus removing the need to form an opening in the sheeting.

Nest box position in relation to gable and frame.

gable end frame

ISOMETRIC SKETCH

Entrance hole flashing pieces to close off corrugation hole position to coincide with trough of sheeting.

corrugated sheeting
sheeting rail
Nest Box

75 × 50 mm steel angle fixed thro to box end panel by 2no 8mm ⌀ bolts with 22mm ⌀ spreader washers, 2no 8mm ⌀ bolts fixed thro sheeting rail.

PLAN

75 × 50 mm steel angle fixed to Zed type rails

nest box

75 × 50mm steel angle fixed to angular rails.

nest box

75×50mm steel angle fixed to timber packing which is bolted into web of Zed type rail

nest box

ALTERNATIVE FIXINGS to sheeting rails

BARN OWL NEST BOX
Alternative methods fixing in Framed Buildings

Prepared at the request of FWAG and the Hawk Trust by ADAS (LAWS) Farm Buildings Group as a contribution to the conservation of the Barn Owl.

not to scale   Aug. 84 a.v.t.
dwg no   BGW 7/01.   01

MAFF
ADAS
LAND AND WATER SERVICE
FARM BUILDINGS GROUP
WOODTHORNE
WOLVERHAMPTON WV6 8TQ
tel (0902) 754190

HISTORICAL
BIBLIOGRAPHY

APLIN, F.C., APLIN, B.D'O., and APLIN, O.V. (1882) *A List of the Birds of The Banbury District*. Banbury: Potts.

APLIN, O.V. (1889) *The Birds of Oxfordshire*. Oxford: Clarendon.

ATKINSON, N. (1974) *Angus Wildlife Review*. 3-4.

BABINGTON, C. (1886) *Catalogue of the Birds of Suffolk*. London: Van Voorst.

BALSTON, R.J., SHEPHERD, C.W., BARTLETT, E. (1907) *Notes on the Birds of Kent*. London: Porter.

BANNERMAN, D.A., and LODGE, G.E. (1955) *The Birds of the British Isles*. Vol IV. Edinburgh and London: Oliver & Boyd.

BARKER, T.W. (1905) *Natural History of Carmarthenshire*. Carmarthen.

BAXTER, E.V., and RINTOUL, L.J. (1928) *The Geographical Distribution and Status of Birds in Scotland*. Edinburgh and London: Oliver & Boyd.

BAXTER, E.V., and RINTOUL, L.J. (1953) *The Birds of Scotland*. Edinburgh and London: Oliver & Boyd.

BECKWITH, W.E. (1879) Birds of Shropshire. *Transactions – Shropshire Archaeological and Natural History Society*. 2: 365-395.

BEWICK, T. (1797) *History of British Birds*. Vol I. Newcastle: Beilby & Bewick; London: Robinson.

BOLAM, G. (1912) *Birds of Northumberland and the Eastern Borders*. Alnwick: Blair.

BORRER, W. (1891) *The Birds of Sussex*. London: Porter.

BRITISH ORNITHOLOGISTS' UNION. (1915) *List of British Birds*. 2nd Ed. London: Wesley.

BROWNE, M. (1907) Birds. In: *The Victoria History of Leicestershire*. Vol I. 114-157. London: Constable.

BUCKNILL, J.A. (1900) *The Birds of Surrey*. London: Porter.

BULL, H.G. (Ed) (1888) *Notes on the Birds of Herefordshire*. London: Hamilton, Adams. Hereford: Jakeman & Carver.

BUND, J.W.W. (1891) *A List of the Birds of Worcestershire and the Adjoining Counties*. Worcester.

CARDIFF NATURALISTS' SOCIETY, (1925) *Birds of Glamorgan*. Exeter: Townsend.

CHRISTY, M. (1890) *The Birds of Essex*. Chelmsford: Durrant. London: Simpkin.

CLARK, J. (1906) Birds. In: *The Victoria History of the County of Cornwall*. Vol I. 309-347. London: Constable.

CLARK KENNEDY, A.W.M.C. (1868) *The Birds of Berkshire and Buckinghamshire*. Eton: Ingalton. London: Simpkin.

COWARD, T.A., and OLDHAM, C. (1900) *The Birds of Cheshire*. Manchester: Sherratt & Hughes.

COWARD, T.A., and OLDHAM, C. (1902) (1904) (1905) Notes on the birds of Anglesey. *The Zoologist*. (401-415) (7-29) (213-230,376-386,423-426).

CRELLIN, R & G. (1944) The barn owl as a resident in the Isle of Man. In: *Bound Pamphlets in Ornithology*.

DAVIS, W.J. (1907) *The Birds of Kent*. Dartford and London: Stock.

DE BUFFON, M. (1770) *Histoire Naturelle Des Oiseaux*. Tome Seizieme. Paris: De L'Imprimerie Royale.

DIXON, C. (1900) *Among the Birds of the Northern Shires*. London: Blackie.

DOBBS, A. (Ed) (1975) *The Birds of Nottinghamshire*. Newton Abbot: David & Charles.

DOBIE, W.H. (1898) Birds of West Cheshire, Denbighshire and Flintshire. *Proceedings of the Chester Society of Natural Science and Literature*. 4, 282-351.

DRUMMOND-HAY, H.M. (1886) Report on the Ornithology of the East of Scotland, from Fife to Aberdeenshire. *Scottish Naturalist*. 2, 355-380.

D'URBAN, W.S.M. and MATHEW, M.A. (1895) *The Birds of Devon*. London: Porter.

DONOVAN, E. (1794-1819) *Natural History of British Birds*. London.

DURNFORD, W.A. (1883) *List of Birds found in the Neighbourhood of Walney Island, with Notes*. Barnsley: Griffiths.

EDWARD, T. (1876) A Revised List of the Birds of Banffshire, with critical notes. In: *Smiles' Life of a Scotch Naturalist*. 394-417. London.

FAWCETT, J.W. (1890) *The Birds of Durham*. Consett: Dent.

FORREST, H.E. (1919) *A Handbook to the Vertebrate Fauna of North Wales*. London: Witherby.

FROST, R. (1978) *Birds of Derbyshire*. Ashbourne: Moorland.

GLADSTONE, H.S. (1910) *The Birds of Dumfriesshire*. London: Witherby.

GLEGG, W.E. (1929) *A History of the Birds of Essex*. London: Witherby.

GLEGG, W.E. (1935) *A History of the Birds of Middlesex*. London: Witherby.

GOODFELLOW, P.F. (1966) The owl enquiry 1959-1964 part one. *Devon Birds*. 19, 20-28.

GRAHAM, H.D. (1890) *The Birds of Iona and Mull 1852-1870*. Edinburgh: Douglas.

GRAY, R., ANDERSON, T. (1869) *The Birds of Ayrshire and Wigtownshire*. Glasgow: Murray.

GRAY, R. (1871) *The Birds of the West of Scotland including the Outer Hebrides*. Glasgow: Murray.

GRAY, R. (1872) The birds of Arran. In: *Geology of Arran and the other Clyde Islands*. Glasgow and London.

GURNEY, J.H. (1884) A catalogue of the birds of Norfolk. In: *History of Norfolk*. (Ed) R.H. Mason. Vol I, Appendices I-XII. London: Westheimer.

HAINES, C.R. (1907) *Notes on the Birds of Rutland*. London: Porter.

HANCOCK, J (1874) A catalogue of the birds of Northumberland and Durham. *Natural History Transactions of Northumberland and Durham*. 6.

HARDING, B.D. (1979) *Bedfordshire Bird Atlas*. Bedfordshire Natural History Society.

HARTERT, E., and JOURDAIN, F.C.R. (1920) *The Birds of Buckinghamshire and the Tring Reservoirs*. Tring: Novitates Zoological.

HARTHAN, A.J. (1947) *The Birds of Worcestershire*. Worcester: Littlebury.

HARVIE-BROWN, J.A., (1888) The Isle of May: its faunal position and bird life. *Proceedings Royal Physiological Society of Edinburgh*. 9, 303-325.

HARVIE-BROWN, J.A., and BUCKLEY, T.E. (1887) *A Vertebrate Fauna of Sutherland, Caithness and West*

Cromarty. Edinburgh: Douglas.

HARVIE-BROWN, J.A., and BUCKLEY, T.E. (1892) *A Vertebrate Fauna of Argyll and the Inner Hebrides.* Edinburgh: Douglas.

HEATHCOTE, A, GRIFFIN, D, MORREY SALMON, H. (Eds) (1967) The birds of Glamorgan. *Transactions of the Cardiff Naturalists' Society.* 94.

HICKLING, R. (1978) *Birds in Leicestershire and Rutland.* Coalville: Leicestershire and Rutland Ornithological Society.

INGRAM, G.C.S. and MORREY SALMON, H. (1963) *The Birds of Monmouthshire.* Newport Museum.

JARDINE, W. (1838) Birds of Great Britain and Ireland – Part I. In: *The Naturalists' Library.* Edinburgh and London: Lizars. Dublin: Curry.

JONES, P.H. and DARE, P. (1976) *Birds of Caernarvonshire.* Cambrian Ornithological Society.

KELSALL, J.E. and MUNN, P.W. (1905) *The Birds of Hampshire and the Isle of Wight.* London: Witherby.

KIRKE NASH, J. (1935) *The Birds of Midlothian.* London: Witherby.

LACK, D. (1934) *The Birds of Cambridgeshire, with an Account of the Birds of the Undrained Fen.* Cambridge: Cambridge Bird Club.

LATHAM, J. (1781-1801) *General Synopsis of Birds.* Vol I. London: White.

LILFORD, Lord. (1885-1897) *Birds of the British Islands.* Vol I. London: Porter.

LILFORD, Lord. (1895) *Notes on the Birds of Northamptonshire and Neighbourhood.* Vol I. London: Porter.

LOCKLEY, R.M., INGRAM, G.C.S., MORREY SALMON, H. (1949) *The Birds of Pembrokeshire.* West Wales Field Society.

LORD, J., and BLAKE, A.R.M. (1962) *The Birds of Staffordshire.* West Midland Bird Club.

LORD, J., and MUNNS D.J. (Eds) (1970) *Atlas of Breeding Birds of the West Midlands.* London: Collins.

MACGILLIVRAY, W. (1836) *Descriptions of the Rapacious Birds of Great Britain.* Edinburgh: Maclachlan and Stewart.

MACGILLIVRAY, W. (1840) *A History of British Birds.* Vol III. London: Scott, Webster and Geary.

MACGIILLIVRAY W. (1846) *A Manual of British Birds.* London: Scott.

MACPHERSON, H.A. (1885-86) The birds of Skye. *Proceedings Royal Physiological Society of Edinburgh.* 9, 118-143.

MACPHERSON, H.A. (1901) Aves. In: *The Victoria History of the County of Cumberland.* Vol I. 179-217. London: Constable.

MACPHERSON, H.A., and DUCKWORTH, W. (1886) *The Birds of Cumberland critically studied, including some Notes on the Birds of Westmorland.* Carlisle: Thurnam.

MANSEL-PLEYDELL, J.C. (1888) *The Birds of Dorsetshire.* London: Porter.

MASEFIELD, J.R.B. (1908) Birds. In: *The Victoria History of the County of Staffordshire.* Vol I. 139-161. London: Constable.

MATHEW, M.A. (1894) *The Birds of Pembrokeshire and its Islands.* London: Porter.

MATHEW, M.A. (1893) A revised list of the birds of Somerset. *Proceedings of the Somerset Natural History and Archaeological Society.* 39, 102-139.

McALDOWIE, A.M. (1893) *The Birds of Staffordshire.* Stoke-upon-Trent: Privately published.

McWILLIAM, J.M. (1936) *The Birds of the Firth of Clyde.* London: Witherby.

McWILLIAM, J.M. (1927) *The Birds of the Island of Bute.* London: Witherby.

MELLERSH, W.L. (1902) *A Treatise on the Birds of Gloucestershire.* Gloucester: Bellows. London: Porter.

MITCHELL, F.S. (1885) *The Birds of Lancashire.* 2nd Ed. rev. by Howard Saunders, 1892. London: Gurney & Jackson.

MONTAGU, G. (1802) *Ornithological Dictionary of British Birds.* Vol I. London: White.

MOORE, R. (1969) *The Birds of Devon.* Newton Abbot: David & Charles.

MUIRHEAD, G. (1889-1895) *The Birds of Berwickshire.* Vols I & II. Edinburgh: Douglas.

NELSON, T.H., EAGLE CLARKE, W., BOYES, F. (1907) *The Birds of Yorkshire.* Vols I & II. London: Brown.

NOBLE, H. (1906) Birds. In: *The Victoria History of the County of Berkshire.* Vol I. 140-166. London: Constable.

NORRIS, C.A. (1947) *Notes on the Birds of Warwickshire.* Birmingham: Cornish.

OAKES, C. (1953) *The Birds of Lancashire.* Edinburgh and London: Oliver & Boyd.

PATON, E.R., and PIKE, O.G. (1929) *The Birds of Ayrshire.* London: Witherby.

PAYN, W.H. (1962) *The Birds of Suffolk.* London: Barrie & Rockliff.

PENHALLURICK, R. (1978) *Birds of Cornwall and the Isles of Scilly.* Penzance: Headland.

PENNANT, T. (1776) *British Zoology.* 4th ed. 1, 176-177. London: White.

PHILLIPS, E.C. (1899) *The Birds of Breconshire.* Brecon: Davies.

PHILLIPS, E.C. (1908) Birds. In: *The Victoria History of the County of Hereford.* Vol I. 130-148. London: Constable.

PIDSLEY, W.E.H. (1891) *The Birds of Devonshire.* (Ed) H.A. MacPherson. London: Gibbings. Exeter: Commin.

RIVIERE, B.B. (1930) *A History of the Birds of Norfolk.* London: Witherby.

RODD, E.H. (1880) *The Birds of Cornwall and the Scilly Islands.* (Ed) J.E. Harting. London: Trubner.

RUTTER, E.M., GRIBBLE, F.C., PEMBERTON, T.W. (1964) *A Handlist of the Birds of Shropshire.* Oswestry: Shropshire Ornithological Society.

ST.JOHN, C.W.G. (1849) *A Tour in Sutherland.* London: Murray.

SAGE, B.L. (1959) *A History of the Birds of Hertfordshire.* London: Barrie & Rockliff.

SAUNDERS, D. (1976) *A Brief Guide to the Birds of Pembrokeshire.* Walters.

SAUNDERS, H. (1899) *An Illustrated Manual of British Birds.* London: Gurney & Jackson.

SCOT-SKIRVING, R. (1878 and 1880) The birds of Islay. *Proceedings Royal Physiological Society of Edinburgh* 4, 69-73; 5, 35-43.

SEEBOHM, H. (1883) *A History of British Birds.* Vol I. London: Porter.

SERVICE, R. (1884) The Birds of Kirkcudbrightshire.

In: *Maxwell's Guide Book to the Stewartry of Kirkcudbright*. Castle Douglas.

SHRUBB, M. (1979) *The Birds of Sussex*. Chichester: Phillimore.

SMITH, A.C. (1887) *The Birds of Wiltshire*. London: Porter. Devizes: Bull.

SMITH, A.E., and CORNWALLIS, R.K. (1955) *The Birds of Lincolnshire*. Lincolnshire Natural History Brochure No.2. Lincoln: Lincolnshire Naturalists' Union.

SMITH, C. (1869) *The Birds of Somersetshire*. London: Van Voorst.

STEELE-ELLIOTT, J. (1904) *The Vertebrate Fauna of Bedfordshire*. Birmingham: Birbeck.

STEVENSON, H. and SOUTHWELL, T. (1866, 1870, 1890) *The Birds of Norfolk*. London: Van Voorst.

TEBBUTT, C.F. (1967) *The Birds of Huntingdonshire*. St Neots: Tebbutt.

THOMPSON, W. (1849) Birds. In: *The Natural History of Ireland*. Vol. 1. London: Reeve.

TICEHURST, C.B. (1932) *A History of the Birds of Suffolk*. London: Gurney & Jackson.

TICEHURST, N.F. (1909) *A History of the Birds of Kent*. London: Witherby.

TOMES, R.F. (1904) Aves. In: *The Victoria History of the County of Warwick*. Vol I. 189-207. London: Constable.

TURNBULL, W.P. (1867) *The Birds of East Lothian and a portion of the Adjoining Counties*. Glasgow: Murray.

USSHER, R.J. (Undated) MSS. Royal Irish Academy.

USSHER, R.J., and WARREN, R. (1900) *The Birds of Ireland*. London: Gurney & Jackson.

WALPOLE-BOND, J.A. (1903) *Birdlife in Wild Wales*. London: Fisher Unwin.

WALPOLE-BOND, J.A. (1938) *A History of Sussex Birds*. Vol II. London: Witherby.

WHITLOCK, F.B. (1893) *The Birds of Derbyshire*. London: Bemrose.

WILSON, J.O. (1933) *Birds of Westmorland and the Northern Pennines*. London: Hutchinson.

YARRELL, W. (1843) *A History of British Birds*. Vol I. London: Van Voorst.

YARRELL, W. and NEWTON A. (1871-1874) *A History of British Birds*. Vol I. London: Van Voorst.

GENERAL
BIBLIOGRAPHY

ANON. (1984) Barn Owl threatened. *Laboratory News.* 306, 1.

ARIB, R. (1979) The Blue List of 1979. *American Birds.* 33, 830-835.

ASHWORTH, B. (1973) The frequency of animal poisoning by warfarin. *Veterinary Record* 93, 50.

BAUDVIN, H. (1975) Biologie de reproduction de la chouette effraie *Tyto alba* en Cote d'Or. *Premiers Resultants le Jean le Blanc.* 14, 1-51.

BEGUIN, J. (1983) *Report on Chemical Control of Voles.* Neuchatel: The Department of Agriculture of the Republic and Canton of Neuchatel.

BENT, A.C. (1961) *Life Histories of North American Birds of Prey.* Part 2. London: Constable.

BEST, R.H. (1976) The changing land-use structure of Britain. *Town and Country Planning* 44, 171-176.

BEST, R.H. (1977) Agricultural land loss – myth or reality? *The Planner* 63, 15-16.

BLAKER, G.B. (1932) Barn Owl and Buzzard. *Bird Notes & News.* 15, 1-4; 34-35.

BLAKER, G.B. (1933) The Barn Owl in England – Results of the Census. *Bird Notes & News.* 15, 169-172; 207-211.

BLAKER, G.B. (1934) *The Barn Owl in England and Wales.* Pamphlet – London: RSPB.

BLAKERS, M., DAVIES, S., and REILLY, P. (1984) *The Atlas of Australian Birds.* Melbourne University Press.

BOARD OF AGRICULTURE AND FISHERIES. (1905) The Barn Owl. *Leaflet No 51.* London: BAF.

BONACINA, L.C.W. (1927) Snowfall in the British Isles during the half-century 1876-1925. *British Rainfall.* 67, 260-287.

BONACINA, L.C.W. (1936) Snowfall in British Isles during decade 1926-1935. *British Rainfall.* 76, 272-292.

BOWMAN, N. (1980) The food of the Barn Owl *Tyto alba* in Mid-Wales. *Nature in Wales.* 17, 84-88.

BOWMAN, N. (1980) The food of Barn Owls *Tyto Alba* at a long-used Pembrokeshire site. *Nature in Wales.* 17, 106-108.

BRAAKSMA, S. and de BRUIJN, O. (1976) De Kerkuilenstand in Nederland. *Limosa.* 49, 135-187.

BRAAKSMA, S. (1980) Gegevens over de achteruitgang van de kerkuil (*Tyto alba guttata* – Brehm) in West-Europa. *Wielewaal.* 46, 421-428.

BROWN, D.J. (1981) Seasonal variations in the prey of some Barn Owls in Gwynedd. *Bird Study.* 28, 139-146.

BUNN, D.S., WARBURTON, A.B., and WILSON, R.D.S. (1982) *The Barn Owl.* Calton: Poyser.

CALVER, M.C., and PORTER, B.D. (1986) Unravelling the food web: dietary analysis in modern ecology. *Journal of Biological Education.* 20, 42-46.

CAMERON COULSON, J. (1950) Tawny Owls found drowned. *British Birds.* 43, 338.

CAMPBELL, B. (1987) Year of the eclipse. *The Countryman.* 92, 38-43.

CENTRAL WATER PLANNING UNIT. (1976) The 1975-76 drought: a hydrological review. *Technical Note No.17.* Reading: Central Water Planning Unit. 38-43.

CHANCELLOR, R.D. (1977) *Report of the Proceedings of the World Conference on Birds of Prey, Vienna 1975.* International Council for Bird Preservation.

CHANDLER, T.J., and GREGORY, S. (1976) *The Climate of the British Isles.* London and New York: Longman.

CHARLES, W.N. (1981) Abundance of Field Voles *Microtus agrestis* in conifer plantations. In: *Forest and Woodland Ecology: An account of research being done in I.T.E.* (Eds) F.T.Last and A.S.Gardiner, 135-137. N.E.R.C.: Institute of Terrestrial Ecology.

CHURCHFIELD, S. (1986) *Shrews.* Mammal Society Series. Oswestry : Nelson.

COLLINGE, W.E. (1924-1927) *The Food of Some British Wild Birds.* pp 178-183. York: privately published.

COLVIN, B.A. (1981) Nest transfer of young Barn Owls. *Ohio Journal of Science.* 81, 132-134.

COLVIN, B.A., HEGDAL, P.L., and JACKSON, W.B. (1984) A comprehensive approach to research and management of Common Barn Owl populations. *Proceedings Workshop on Management of Nongame Species and Ecological Communities, Lexington, Kentucky.*

COLVIN, B.A. (1985) Common Barn-Owl population decline in Ohio and the relationship to agricultural trends. *Journal of Field Ornithology.* 56, 224-235.

CONGREVE, W.M. (1950) Tawny Owls found drowned. *British Birds.* 43, 338-339.

CONTOLI, L. (1975) Micro-mammals and environment in central Italy: Data from *Tyto alba* (Scop) pellets. *Bulletin Zoology.* 42, 223-229.

CONTOLI, L., and SAMMURI, G. (1978) Predation on small mammals by Tawny Owl and comparison with Barn Owl in the Farma valley (central Italy). *Bulletin Zoology.* 45, 323-335.

CONTOLI, L. (1984) Owl pellets as an indirect sampling source for terrestrial small mammal populations. *4th Simposio Dinamica Popolazioni (Parma 22-24 ottobre 1981)* 167-176.

CONTOLI, L., MARENZI, A.R., and NAPOLEONE, I. (1985) Une banque de donnees sur les systemes trophiques <rapaces-petits mammiferes terrestres>. *Bulletin Zoology.* 52, 309-321.

COOKE, A.S., BELL, A.A., and HAAS, M.B. (1982) *Predatory Birds, Pesticides and Pollution.* Cambridge: Institute of Terrestrial Ecology.

COPPOCK, J.T. (1976) *An Agricultural Atlas of England and Wales.* London: Faber & Faber.

CORBET, G.B., and SOUTHERN, H.N. (Eds) (1977) *The Handbook of British Mammals.* Oxford: Blackwell Scientific.

CRAMP, S. (1963) Toxic chemicals and birds of prey. *British Birds.* 56, 124-139.

CRAMP, S. (Ed) (1985) *The Birds of the Western Palearctic.* Vol IV. Oxford and New York: Oxford University Press.

CURTIS, L.F., COURTNEY, F.M., and TRUDGILL, S.T. (1976) *Soils in the British Isles.* London and New York: Longman.

DARLEY, G. (1981) *The National Trust Book of The Farm.* London: The National Trust and Weidenfeld & Nicholson.

De JONG, J. (1985) In Friesland hebben de kerkuilen het

goed. *Vogels.* 30, 206-207.

DICKMAN, C.R. (1980) Estimation of population density in the Common Shrew, *Sorex araneus*, from a conifer plantation. *Journal of Zoology, London.* 192, 550-552.

DINAN, J., and WINGFIELD, G. (1985) Regional Reports – Nebraska. *The Eyas.* 8, 7-9.

DOBINSON, H.M., and RICHARDS, A.J. (1964) The effects of the severe winter of 1962/63 on birds in Britain. *British Birds.* 57, 373-433.

DUCKETT, J.E. (1981) Barn Owls (*Tyto alba*) – a proven natural predator of rats in oil palm. In: *'The Oil Palm in Agriculture in the Eighties'* 2, 461-473. Eds. E. Pushparajah and Chew Poh Soon. Kuala Lumpur: Incorporated Society of Planters.

DUCKETT, J.E. (1984) Barn Owls (*Tyto alba*) and the 'second generation' rat-baits utilised in oil palm plantations in Peninsular Malaysia. *Planter, Kuala Lumpur.* 60, 3-11.

ELTON, C. (1965) *Voles, Mice and Lemmings.* (Reprint) Codicote: Wheldon & Wesley.

ERLICHMAN, J. (1984) Barn Owl defenders smell a rat. *The Guardian.* 18th June.

EVERETT, M. (1977) *A natural history of Owls.* London: Hamlyn.

FAIRLEY, J.S. (1966) Analyses of Barn Owl pellets from an Irish roost. *British Birds.* 59, 338-340.

FAIRLEY, J.S., and DEANE, C.D. (1967) Analysis of Barn Owl pellets from Co. Fermanagh. *British Birds.* 60, 370.

FLOWERDEW, J. (1984) *Woodmice.* Mammal Society Series. Oswestry: Nelson.

FRANK, F. (1957) The causality of microtine cycles in Germany. *The Journal of Wildlife Management.* 21, 113-121.

FRYLESTAM, B. (1972) Uber Wanderungen und Sterblichkeit Beringter Skandinavischer Schleiereulen *Tyto alba. Ornis Scandinavica.* 3, 45-54.

FULLER, R.J. (1982) *Bird Habitats in Britain.* Calton: Poyser.

FUSSELL, G.E. (1966) *Farming Technique from Prehistoric to Modern Times.*

GALUSHIN, V.M. (1974) Synchronous fluctuations in populations of some raptors and their prey. *The Ibis.* 116, 127-134.

GAME CONSERVANCY, THE (1986) *Hedgerows and Headlands for Wildlife.* (Leaflet).

GELAC GROUP. (1984) *GELAC Trial: General Report on the Three Operating Phases – Autumn 1981/Spring – Autumn 1982.* La Chaux-de-Fonds: GELAC.

GIPPS, J., ALIBHAI, S., GURNELL, J., and KREBS, C. (1986) A plague of voles: the search for a cure. *New Scientist.* 111, 48-51.

GLUE, D.E. (1967) Prey taken by the Barn Owl in England and Wales. *Bird Study.* 14, 169-183.

GLUE, D.E. (1971) Avian predator pellet analysis and the mammalogist. *Mammal Review.* 1, 53-62.

GLUE, D.E. (1971) Ringing recovery circumstances of small birds of prey. *Bird Study.* 18, 137-146.

GLUE, D.E., and NUTTALL, J. (1971) Adverse climatic conditions affecting the diet of a Barn Owl in Lancashire. *Bird Study.* 18, 33-34.

GLUE, D.E. (1972) Bird prey taken by British Owls. *Bird Study.* 19, 91-95.

GLUE, D.E. (1973) Seasonal mortality in four small birds of prey. *Ornis Scandinavica.* 4, 97-102.

GLUE, D.E. (1974) Food of the Barn Owl in Britain and Ireland. *Bird Study.* 21, 200-210.

GLUE, D.E. (1975) Harvest mice as Barn Owl prey in the British Isles. *Mammal Review.* 5, 9-12.

GROLLEAU, G. (1983) Le rodenticide anticoagulant Bromadiolone est-il dangereux pour les animaux predateurs et en particulier les rapaces? *La Defense des Vegetaux.* 219, 14-22.

GROLLEAU, G., and LORGUE, G. (1984) Secondary toxicity of an anticoagulant rodenticide – Bromadiolone – for the Common Buzzard *Buteo buteo* – experimental study. *The International Symposium of Terrestrial Ecotoxicology. Les Arcs, Savoy.* 12-14 December 1984.

HAMMOND, N. (1980) Putting order into Law. *Birds.* 8, 51-53.

HARDY, A.R., HIRONS, G.J.M., and STANLEY, P.I. (1981) The relationship of body weight, fat deposit and moult to the reproductive cycles in wild tawny owls and barn owls. In: *Recent Advances in the Study of Raptor Diseases.* 159-163. (Eds) J.E. Cooper and A.G. Greenwood. Keighley: Chirons.

HARDY, A.R., HIRONS, G.J.M., STANLEY, P.I., and HUSON, L.W. (1981) Sexual dimorphism in size of Tawny Owls *Strix aluco*: A method for sexing in field studies. *Ardea.* 69, 181-184.

HARGREAVES, M.I. (1976) Statistics of snow depth at selected stations in England, Wales and Northern Ireland. November 1946-April 1973. *Climatological Memorandum 76.* Bracknell: Meteorological Office (Met.0.3).

HEGDAL, P.L., and BLASKIEWICZ, R.W. (1984) Evaluation of the potential hazard to Barn Owls of Talon (brodifacoum bait) used to control rats and house mice. *Environmental Toxicology and Chemistry* 3, 167-179.

HENNY, C.J. (1969) Geographical variation in mortality rates and production requirements of the Barn Owl *Tyto alba. Bird Banding.* 40, 277-356.

HERBST, P.H., BREDENKAMP, D.B., and BARKER, H.M.G. (1966) A technique for the evaluation of drought from rainfall data. *Journal of Hydrology.* 4, 264-272.

HICKLING, R. (1983) *Enjoying Ornithology.* Calton: Poyser.

HIRONS, G.J.M., HARDY, A.R., and STANLEY, P.I. (1979) Starvation in young tawny owls. *Bird Study.* 26, 59-63.

HIRONS, G.J.M., HARDY, A.R., and STANLEY, P.I. (1984) Body weight, gonad development and moult in the Tawny Owl *Strix aluco. Journal of Zoology, London.* 202, 145-164.

HIRONS, G.J.M. (1985) The importance of body reserves for successful reproduction in the Tawny Owl *Strix aluco. Journal of Zoology, London – Series B.* 1, 1-20.

HIRSCHFELD, E. (1974-1975) *Projekt Tornuggla.* Leaflet.

HIRSCHFELD, E. (1981) Project Barn Owl. *Var Fagelvarld* 40, 343-344.

HMSO (1968) *A Century of Agricultural Statistics.* London: HMSO.

HMSO (1986) *Agricultural Statistics United Kingdom 1984.* London: HMSO.

HONER, M.R. (1963) Observations on the Barn Owl *Tyto alba guttata* in the Netherlands in relation to its ecology and population fluctuations. *Ardea.* 51, 158-195.

HUNTING SURVEYS (1986) *Monitoring Landscape Change.* Vols 1 and 1a. Borehamwood: Hunting Surveys and Consultants Limited.

ICBP (1964) *Working Conference on Birds of Prey and Owls.* London: International Council for Bird Preservation.

ICI. (Undated) *Brodifacoum Rodenticide – A Selection of Published Information.* ICI: Plant Protection Division.

JENKINSON, R.D.S., and GILBERTSON, D.D. (1984) *In the Shadow of Extinction.* Nottinghamshire and Derbyshire County Council.

JOURDAIN, F.C.R., and WITHERBY, H.F. (1918) The effect of the winter of 1916-1917 on our resident birds. *British Birds.* 11, 266-271; 12, 26-35.

JUILLARD, M., and BEURET, J. (1983) L'amenagement de sites de nidification et son influence sur une population de Chouettes effraies, *Tyto alba*, dans le nord-ouest de la Suisse. *Nos Oiseaux* 37, 1-20.

KENNEDY, R.J. (1975) Barn Owl Survey Progress Report for 1975. *Bird-Ringing in South West Lancashire.*

KING, A., and CLIFFORD, S. (1985) *Holding Your Ground.* London: Temple Smith.

KNIGHT, R.L., and JACKMAN, R.E. (1984) Food-niche relationships between Great Horned Owls and Common Barn-Owls in Eastern Washington. *The Auk.* 101, 175-179.

LACK, P. (1986) *The Atlas of Wintering Birds in Britain and Ireland.* Calton: Poyser.

LAMB, H.H. (1965) Britain's changing climate. In: *The Biological Significance of Climatic Changes in Britain. Institute of Biology. Symposia No.14.* London: Academic Press.

LAMB, H.H. (1970) Our changing climate. In: *The Flora of a Changing Britain.* (Ed) F. Perring. London: Botanical Society of the British Isles.

LANGE, P.F., and TERVEER, J. (1954) Warfarin poisoning. Report of fourteen cases. *U.S. Armed Forces Medical Journal.* 5, 872-877.

LENTON, G.M. (1978) Owls as rat controllers – a preliminary report. *Planter, Kuala Lumpur.* 54, 72-83.

LENTON, G.M. (1980) Biological control of rats in oil palm by owls. *Tropical Ecology & Development.* 615-621.

LENTON, G.M. (1983) Wise owls flourish among the oil palms. *New Scientist.* 97, 436-437.

LENTON, G.M. (1984) The feeding and breeding ecology of Barn Owls *Tyto alba* in Peninsular Malaysia. *Ibis.* 126, 551-575.

LENTON, G.M. (1985) History, distribution and origin of Barn Owls *Tyto alba* in the Malay Peninsula. *Bulletin British Ornithologists' Club.* 105, 54-58.

LESLIE, P.H., VENABLES, U.M., and VENABLES, L.S.V. (1952) The fertility and population structure of the Brown Rat *Rattus norvegicus* in corn-ricks and some other habitats. *Proceedings of the Zoological Society of London.* 122, 187-238.

LIPPENS, L., WILLE, H. (1972) *Atals van de Vogels in Belgie in West-Europa.* Tielt: Lannoo.

LOCKIE, J.D. (1955) The breeding habits and food of Short-eared Owls after a vole plague. *Bird Study.* 2, 53-69.

LORGUE, G. (1982) Toxicologie des raticides anti-coagulants. *La Defense des Vegetaux.* 215, 118-123.

LOVARI, S., RENZONI, A., and FONDI, R. (1976) The predatory habits of the Barn Owl *Tyto alba* Scopoli in relation to the vegetation cover. *Bulletin of Zoology.* 43, 173-191.

MACDONALD, J.W. (1965) Mortality in wild birds. *Bird Study.* 12, 181-194.

MAFF/ADAS. (1982) Secondary toxicity hazard to owls from difenacoum. Research and Development Report: Pesticide Science 1981. *Reference Book of MAFF* 252 (81) 36-38. London: HMSO.

MAFF/ADAS. (1984) Biochemical studies on the mechanism of resistance to anticoagulant rodenticides in rats and mice. Research and Development Report: Pesticide Science 1983. *Reference Book of MAFF* 252 (83) 52-54. London: HMSO.

MAFF (1986) *Data Requirements for Approval under the Control of Pesticides Regulations 1986.* Harpenden: MAFF.

MALE, A.E. (1950) Tawny Owls found drowned. *British Birds.* 43, 157.

MARSH, T. and LEES, M. (1986) The 1984 drought. *Hydrological Data: UK series.* Institute of Hydrology.

MARTIN, J. (1984) Results of the Suffolk Barn Owl enquiry 1983. *Suffolk Ornithologists Group Bulletin.* 64, 5-13.

MAXWELL, R.I. (1977) *Farmland Tree Survey of Norfolk.* Norfolk County Council.

MEAD, C., and SMITH, K. (1982) *The Hertfordshire Breeding Bird Atlas.* Tring: HBBA.

MEAD, C.J., and HUDSON, R. (1983) Report on bird-ringing for 1982. *Ringing and Migration.* 4, 281-285.

MEAD, C.J., and HUDSON, R. (1984) Report on bird-ringing for 1983. *Ringing and Migration.* 5, 153-159.

MEADEN, G.T. (1976) North-west Europe's great drought – the worst in Britain since 1252-1253? *The Journal of Meteorology.* 1, 379-383.

MEEHAN, A.P. (1984) *Rats and Mice – Their biology and control.* East Grinstead: Rentokil Ltd.

MELLANBY, K. (1981) *Farming and Wildlife.* London: Collins.

MENDENHALL, V.M., and PANK, L.F. (1980) Secondary poisoning of owls by anticoagulant rodenticides. *Wildlife Society Bulletin.* 8, 311-315.

MENDENHALL, V.M., KLAAS, E.E., and McLANE, M.A.R. (1983) Breeding success of Barn Owls *Tyto alba* fed low levels of DDE and Dieldrin. *Archives of Environmental Contamination and Toxicology.* 12, 235-240.

MERSON, M.H., BYERS, R.E., and KAUKEINEN, D.E. (1984) Residues of the rodenticide brodifacoum in voles and raptors after orchard treatment. *Journal of Wildlife Management.* 48, 212-216.

METEOROLOGICAL OFFICE. (1952) *Climatological Atlas of the British Isles.* London: HMSO.

METEOROLOGICAL OFFICE. (1975) Maps of mean and extreme temperature over the United Kingdom 1941-1970. *Climatological Memorandum No. 73.* Bracknell: Meteorological Office (Met.0.3).

METEOROLOGICAL OFFICE. (1975) Maps of mean number of days of snow over the United Kingdom

1941-1970. *Climatological Memorandum No. 74*. Bracknell: Meteorological Office (Met.0.3).

METEOROLOGICAL OFFICE. (1977) Map of *Average Annual Rainfall – International Standard Period 1941-1970*. Bracknell: Meteorological Office (Met 0.866 (SB)).

METEOROLOGICAL OFFICE. (1980) *Addendum to Climatological Memorandum No.76*. Bracknell: Meteorological Office (Met.0.3b).

METEOROLOGICAL OFFICE. (1985) *Snow Survey of Great Britain 1983/84*. Bracknell: Meteorological Office.

MIKKOLA, H. (1976) Owls killing and killed by other owls and raptors in Europe. *British Birds*. 69, 144-154.

MIKKOLA, H. (1983) *Owls of Europe*. Calton: Poyser.

MITCHELL, J., PLACIDO, C., and ROSE, R. (1974) Notes on a Short-tailed Vole plague at Eskdalemuir, Dumfries-shire. *Transactions of the Dumfries and Galloway Natural History and Antiquarian Society*. 2, 11-13.

MOORE, N.W. (1957) The past and present status of the Buzzard in the British Isles. *British Birds*. 50, 173-197.

MOORE, N.W. (1965) Pesticides and birds – a review of the situation in Great Britain in 1965. *Bird Study*. 12, 222-252.

MORTIMORE, K.O. (1976) The great drought 1975-1976. *The Journal of Meteorology*. 1, 373-378.

MULLIE, W.C., and MEININGER, P.L. (1985) The decline of bird of prey populations in Egypt. In: *Conservation Studies on Raptors*. (Eds) I. Newton and R.D. Chancellor. Cambridge: International Council for Bird Preservation.

MYERS, J.H., and KREBS, C.J. (1974) Population Cycles in Rodents. *Scientific American*. 230, 38-46.

NEWHOUSE, D.A., and EHRESMAN, B.L. (1983) *The Common Barn Owl*. Leaflet. Iowa Conservation Commission.

NEWTON, I. (1979) *Population Ecology of Raptors*. Berkhamsted: Poyser.

NEWTON, I., BELL, A.A., and WYLLIE, I. (1982) Mortality of Sparrowhawks and Kestrels. *British Birds*. 75, 195-204.

NEWTON, I. (1984) Raptors in Britain – a review of the last 150 years. *BTO News*. 131, 6-7.

NEWTON,I., and HAAS, M.B. (1984) The return of the Sparrowhawk. *British Birds*. 77, 47-70.

NEWTON, I., and CHANCELLOR, R.D. (Eds) (1985) *Conservation Studies on Raptors*. Cambridge: International Council for Bird Preservation.

O'CONNOR, R.J., and SHRUBB, M. (1983) Some effects of agricultural development on British bird populations. *Proceedings – Symposium Birds and Man, Johannesburg*.

O'CONNOR, R.J., and SHRUBB, M. (1986) *Farming and Birds*. Cambridge: Cambridge University Press.

OLNEY, P.J.S. (Ed) (1984) *1983 International Zoo Yearbook*. Vol 23. London: Zoological Society of London.

ORCHEL, J. (1985/6) Barn Owl conservation in Galloway: 1983-86. *The Hawk Trust Annual Report*. 15, 6-7.

ORCHEL, J. (1986) *Barn Owl study and Conservation Project by the Hawk Trust: West Galloway 1986*. London: The Hawk Trust.

OSBORNE, L., and KREBS, J. (1981) Replanting after Dutch elm disease. *New Scientist*. 90, 212-215.

OSBORNE, P. (1982) Some effects of Dutch elm disease on nesting farmland birds. *Bird Study*. 29, 2-16.

PALMA, L. (1985) The present situation of birds of prey in Portugal. In: *Conservation Studies on Raptors*. (Eds) I. Newton and R.D. Chancellor. Cambridge: International Council for Bird Preservation.

PARSLOW, J. (1973) *Breeding Birds of Britain and Ireland*. Berkhamsted: Poyser.

PEDROLI, J.C. (1983) Control of the Field Vole. *Report of the Neuchatel Canton Fishing and Hunting Service*. Neuchatel.

PETERSEN, L.R. (1980) Status of Barn Owls in Wisconsin, 1979. *Department of Natural Resources Research*. Report 107. Wisconsin: Department of Natural Resources.

PETTY, S.J. (1987) Breeding of Tawny Owls *Strix aluco* in relation to their food supply in an upland forest. In: *Reproduction and Breeding in Birds of Prey*.

PHILIPPE, J. (1983) *Luttes chimiques contre les rongeurs sauvages*. Thesis, L'Universite Claude Bernard de Lyon.

PICOZZI, N., and HEWSON, R. (1970) Kestrels, short-eared owls and field voles in Eskdalemuir in 1970. *Scottish Birds*. 6, 185-191.

PIKULA, J., BEKLOVA, M., and KUBIK, V. (1984) The breeding bionomy of *Tyto alba*. *Prirodoved Pr Ustavu Cesk Akad Ved Brne*. 18, 1-56.

PIECHOCKI, R. (1960) Uber die Winterverluste bei Schleireulen *Tyto alba Vogelwarte* 20 274-280.

PILE, C.G. (1958) The Barn Owl. *Bulletin of the Societe Jersiaise*. 17, 187-190.

POLLARD, E., HOOPER, M.D., and MOORE, N.W. (Eds) (1974) *Hedges*. London: Collins.

PRESTT, I. (1965) An enquiry into the recent breeding status of some of the smaller birds of prey and crows in Britain. *Bird Study*. 12, 196-220.

PRESTT, I., and BELL, A.A. (1966) An objective method of recording breeding distribution of common birds of prey in Britain. *Bird Study*. 13, 277-283.

PRZYGODDA, W. (1964) Rodenticides and birds of prey. Report on *Working Conference on Birds of Prey and Owls – Caen*. 58-61. London: International Council for Bird Preservation.

RACKHAM, O. (1986) *The History of the Countryside*. London: Dent.

RADVANYI, A. (1982) Secondary poisoning effects of anticoagulants on raptors. *Paper presented at The Third International Theriological Congress, Helsinki* (proceedings in press).

RAMMELL, C.G., HOOGENBOOM, J.J.L., COTTER, M., WILLIAMS, J.M., and BELL, J. (1984) Brodifacoum residues in target and non-target animals following rabbit poisoning trials. *New Zealand Journal of Experimental Agriculture* 12, 107-111.

RATCLIFFE, D. (1980) *The Peregrine Falcon*. Calton: Poyser.

RATCLIFFE, E.J. (1979) *Fly High, Run Free*. London: Chatto and Windus.

RATCLIFFE, P.R., and PETTY, S.J. (1986) The management of commercial forests for wildlife. In: *Trees and Wildlife in the Scottish Uplands*. (Ed) D. Jenkins. Cambridge: Institute of Terrestrial Ecology.

RICHARDS, C.G.J. (1985) The population dynamics of *Microtus agrestis* in Wytham, 1949 to 1978. *Acta Zoologica Fennica.* 173, 35-38.

ROBINSON, P. (1894) *Birds of the Wave and Woodland.* London.

RYVES, B.H. (1950) Tawny owls found drowned. *British Birds.* 43, 338.

SANDISON, R.J. (1980) Barn Owls in Sussex – the last twelve years. *The Sussex Bird Report.* 33, 70-78.

SCHIFFERLI, A. (1957) Alter und Sterblichkeit bei Waldkauz (*Strix aluco*) und Schleiereule (*Tyto alba*) in der Schweiz. *Ornith. Beobachter.* 54, 50-56.

SCHONFELD, M., GIRBIG, G., and STURM, H. (1977) Beitrage zur Populations dynamik der Schleiereule *Tyto alba. Hercynia* 14, 303-51.

SECRETT, C., and CLIFF HODGES, V. (1986) *Motorway Madness.* London: Friends of the Earth.

SEEL, D.C., THOMSON, A.G., and TURNER, J.C.E. (1983) *Distribution and Breeding of the Barn Owl (Tyto Alba) on Anglesey, North Wales.* Bangor Occasional Paper No 16. Bangor: Institute of Terrestrial Ecology.

SHARROCK, J.T.R. (1976) *The Atlas of Breeding Birds in Britain and Ireland.* Tring: British Trust for Ornithology.

SHAWYER, C.R. (1985) *Rodenticides: A Review and Assessment of their Potential Hazard to Non-Target Wildlife with Special Reference to The Barn Owl Tyto alba.* London: The Hawk Trust.

SHRUBB, M. (1982) The hunting behaviour of some farmland kestrels. *Bird Study.* 29, 121-128.

SHRUBB, M. (1984) Food and hunting in a farmland raptore population. *The Sussex Bird Report.* 37, 84-90.

SIMEONOV, S.D., MICHEV, T.M., and SIMEONOV, P.S. (1981) Materials on the nesting distribution and the diet of the Barn Owl *Tyto alba* in Bulgaria. *Ekologiya Sofiya* 8, 49-54.

SMAL, C.M. (1987) The diet of the Barn Owl *Tyto alba* in southern Ireland, with reference to a recently introduced prey species – the Bank Vole *Clethrionomys glareolus. Bird Study.* 34, 113-125.

SMITH, W. (1985) Regional Report – Midwest. *The Eyas.* 8, 7-8.

SMITH, W. (1986) Regional Report – Midwest. *The Eyas.* 9, 8-19.

SMYTH, M. (1966) Winter breeding in woodland mice, *Apodemus sylvaticus* and voles *Clethrionomys glareolus* and *Microtus agrestis*, near Oxford. *Journal of Animal Ecology.* 35, 471-485.

SNOW, D.W. (1968) Movements and mortality of British kestrels *Falco tinnunculus. Bird Study.* 15, 65-83.

SOUTHERN, H.N. (1954) Tawny owls and their prey. *Ibis.* 96, 384-410.

SOUTHERN, H.N., VAUGHAN, R., and MUIR, R.C. (1954) The behaviour of young tawny owls after fledging. *Bird Study.* 1, 101-110.

SOUTHERN, H.N. (1959) Mortality and population control. *Ibis.* 101, 429-436.

SOUTHERN, H.N., and LOWE, V.P.W. (1968) The pattern of distribution of prey and predation in tawny owl territories. *Journal of Animal Ecology.* 37, 75-97.

SOUTHERN, H.N. (1969) Prey taken by tawny owls during the breeding season. *Ibis.* 111, 293-299.

SOUTHERN, H.N. (1970) The natural control of a population of tawny owls *Strix aluco. Journal of Zoology. London.* 162, 197-285.

SPARKS, J., and SOPER, T. (1982) *Owls – Their Natural and Unnatural History.* Newton Abbot: David & Charles.

SPENCER, K.G. (1965) Avian casualties on railways. *Bird Study.* 12, 257.

SPENCER, R. (1968) Report on bird ringing for 1967. *British Birds.* 61, 477-523.

SPENCER, R., and HUDSON, R. (1982) Report on bird-ringing for 1981. *Ringing and Migration.* 4, 65-68.

STANLEY, P.I., and ELLIOTT, G.R. (1976) An assessment based on residues in owls of environmental contamination arising from the use of mercury compounds in British agriculture. *Agro-Ecosystems.* 2, 223-234.

STIRLING, R. (1982) *The Weather of Britain.* London: Faber and Faber.

TATE, J. (1981) The Blue List for 1981. *American Birds.* 35, 3-10.

TAYLOR, K., FULLER, R.J., and LACK, P.C. (Eds) (1985) Bird census and atlas studies. *Proceedings of the VIII International Conference on Bird Census and Atlas Work.* Tring: British Trust for Ornithology.

TAYLOR, I.R. (1984) *Presentation to Bird of Prey Conference, British Trust for Ornithology, Swanwick. 17th-19th February 1984.*

THOM, V.M. (1986) *Birds in Scotland.* Calton: Poyser.

TICEHURST, C.B. (1935) On the food of the Barn Owl and its bearing on Barn Owl population. *Ibis.* 5, 329-335.

TICEHURST, N.F., and HARTLEY, P.H.T. (1948) Report on the effect of the severe winter of 1946-1947 on bird-life. *British Birds.* 41, 322-334.

TICEHURST, N.F., and WITHERBY, H.F. (1940) Report on the effect of the severe winter of 1939-40 on bird-life in the British Isles. *British Birds.* 34, 118-132 and 142-155.

TOMLINSON, D. (1984) Barn Owls and poisons. *Country Life.* 7th June.

TOWNSEND, M.G., FLETCHER, M.R., ODAM, E.M., and STANLEY, P.I. (1981) An assessment of the secondary poisoning hazard of warfarin to Tawny Owls. *Journal of Wildlife Management.* 45, 242-248.

TWIGG, G. (1975) *The Brown Rat.* Newton Abbot: David & Charles.

VAURIE, C. (1965) *The Birds of the Palearctic Fauna.* London: Witherby.

VENABLES, L.S.V., and LESLIE, P.H. (1942) The rat and mouse populations of corn ricks. *Journal of Animal Ecology.* 11, 44-68.

VERNON, J.D.R. (1972) Prey taken by Short-eared Owls in winter quarters in Britain. *Bird Study.* 19, 114-115.

VILLAGE, A. (1981) The diet and breeding of long-eared owls in relation to vole numbers. *Bird Study.* 28, 215-224.

VILLAGE, A. (1986) Breeding performance of Kestrels at Eskdalemuir, South Scotland. *Journal of Zoology (A)* 208, 367-378.

VOOUS, K.H. (1960) *Atlas of European Birds.* London: Nelson.

WARBURTON, A. (1984) Breeding and reintroduction of the Barn Owl *Tyto alba.* In: *International Zoo*

Yearbook 23. (Ed) P.J.S. Olney. pp. 88-95. London: Zoological Society of London.

WATSON, D. (1977) *The Hen Harrier.* Berkhamsted: Poyser.

WEBSTER, J.A. (1973) Seasonal variation in mammal contents of Barn Owl castings. *Bird Study.* 20, 185-196.

WEIR, D.N. (1971) Mortality of hawks and owls in Speyside. *Bird Study.* 18, 147-154.

WENDLAND, V. (1984) The influence of prey fluctuations on the breeding success of the Tawny Owl *Strix aluco. Ibis.* 126, 284-295.

WENZ, C. (1984) New chemicals under fire. *Nature.* 309, 741.

WILKINSON, G. (1978) *Epitaph for the Elm.* London: Hutchinson.

WITHERBY, H.F. (1908-1909) A plan for marking birds. *British Birds.* 2, 35.

WITHERBY, H.F., and JOURDAIN, F.C.R. (1929) Report on the effect of severe weather in 1929 on bird-life. *British Birds.* 23, 154-158.

WITHERBY, H.F., JOURDAIN, F.C.R., TICE-HURST N.F., and TUCKER, B.W. (1943) *The Handbook of British Birds.* Vol II. Revised Edition. London: Witherby.

ZIESEMER, F. (1980) Verbreitung, Siedlungsdichte und Bestandsentwicklung der Schleiereule *Tyto alba* in Schleswig-Holstein. *Corax.* 8, 107-130.

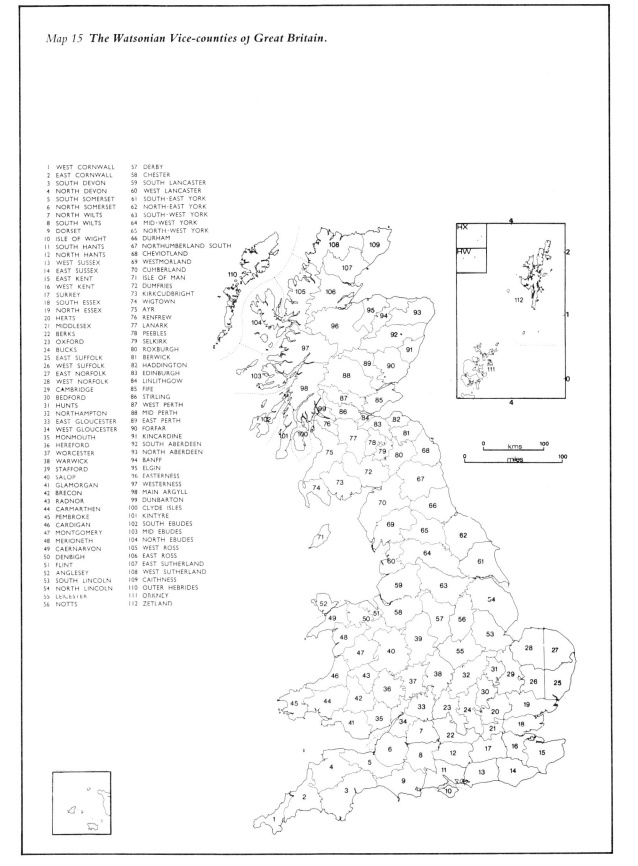

Map 15 *The Watsonian Vice-counties of Great Britain.*

1	WEST CORNWALL	57	DERBY
2	EAST CORNWALL	58	CHESTER
3	SOUTH DEVON	59	SOUTH LANCASTER
4	NORTH DEVON	60	WEST LANCASTER
5	SOUTH SOMERSET	61	SOUTH-EAST YORK
6	NORTH SOMERSET	62	NORTH-EAST YORK
7	NORTH WILTS	63	SOUTH-WEST YORK
8	SOUTH WILTS	64	MID-WEST YORK
9	DORSET	65	NORTH-WEST YORK
10	ISLE OF WIGHT	66	DURHAM
11	SOUTH HANTS	67	NORTHUMBERLAND SOUTH
12	NORTH HANTS	68	CHEVIOTLAND
13	WEST SUSSEX	69	WESTMORLAND
14	EAST SUSSEX	70	CUMBERLAND
15	EAST KENT	71	ISLE OF MAN
16	WEST KENT	72	DUMFRIES
17	SURREY	73	KIRKCUDBRIGHT
18	SOUTH ESSEX	74	WIGTOWN
19	NORTH ESSEX	75	AYR
20	HERTS	76	RENFREW
21	MIDDLESEX	77	LANARK
22	BERKS	78	PEEBLES
23	OXFORD	79	SELKIRK
24	BUCKS	80	ROXBURGH
25	EAST SUFFOLK	81	BERWICK
26	WEST SUFFOLK	82	HADDINGTON
27	EAST NORFOLK	83	EDINBURGH
28	WEST NORFOLK	84	LINLITHGOW
29	CAMBRIDGE	85	FIFE
30	BEDFORD	86	STIRLING
31	HUNTS	87	WEST PERTH
32	NORTHAMPTON	88	MID PERTH
33	EAST GLOUCESTER	89	EAST PERTH
34	WEST GLOUCESTER	90	FORFAR
35	MONMOUTH	91	KINCARDINE
36	HEREFORD	92	SOUTH ABERDEEN
37	WORCESTER	93	NORTH ABERDEEN
38	WARWICK	94	BANFF
39	STAFFORD	95	ELGIN
40	SALOP	96	EASTERNESS
41	GLAMORGAN	97	WESTERNESS
42	BRECON	98	MAIN ARGYLL
43	RADNOR	99	DUNBARTON
44	CARMARTHEN	100	CLYDE ISLES
45	PEMBROKE	101	KINTYRE
46	CARDIGAN	102	SOUTH EBUDES
47	MONTGOMERY	103	MID EBUDES
48	MERIONETH	104	NORTH EBUDES
49	CAERNARVON	105	WEST ROSS
50	DENBIGH	106	EAST ROSS
51	FLINT	107	EAST SUTHERLAND
52	ANGLESEY	108	WEST SUTHERLAND
53	SOUTH LINCOLN	109	CAITHNESS
54	NORTH LINCOLN	110	OUTER HEBRIDES
55	LEICESTER	111	ORKNEY
56	NOTTS	112	ZETLAND

113